PRINTER'S PROGRESS

1851-1951

PRINTER'S PROGRESS

BY

CHARLES ROSNER

A COMPARATIVE SURVEY

OF THE CRAFT OF PRINTING

1851 – 1951

CAMBRIDGE

HARVARD UNIVERSITY PRESS

1951

First published in 1951
by Sylvan Press Limited, London
and Harvard University Press, Cambridge, Mass.
Designed and printed by Balding & Mansell Limited
London and Wisbech

MADE IN GREAT BRITAIN

PRO DOMO

I wish to express my great gratitude to my friends in many countries who, with suggestions, advice and help, have made it possible to present the printers' case in its manifold aspects. It would be a major omission on my part not to thank at the same time all those whose technical ability has proved so valuable in the production of this book and whose names are listed in the colophon.

The material for documentation has been chosen as being representative of both 1851 and 1951. A substantial part of the contemporary matter has been specially designed to demonstrate the various printing methods of today.

The choice of designers was determined by their experience of reproduction techniques gained by working in close co-operation with printers.

C. R.

1 - 2

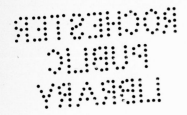

ROSNER, CHARLES. Printer's progress; a comparative survey of the craft of printing, 1851-1951. 119p il col il $5 Harvard univ. press

655.1   Printing—History   [51-14375]

"This volume is a comparison between the printer of 1851 and the printer of 1951, and of the work and tools representative of each. . . Ignoring the phases between 1851 and 1951, Mr. Rosner is able to make strikingly evident the progress achieved in one hundred years. Vast changes have been wrought in machinery and materials during this time, particularly following the advent of the camera. This latter invention has resulted in such techniques as older printers could only dream of: photoengraving, photolithography, photogravure, photocomposing, etc. Such advances have almost without exception improved the craft to such a degree that today it might in many cases be called, and with justification, an art." Special Libraries

"Unfortunately, in developing his idea, [Mr Rosner] has permitted his obvious predilection for so-called contemporary forms of graphic design to give an ill-balanced comparison between 1851 and our own time. . . The book is well produced, although there is a certain flatness in the lithographic sections. Mr. Ellic Howe's scholarly touch is happily evident in the brief introductory notes." Robert Harling

Spec 187:516 O 19 '51 600w

Special Libraries 43:32 Ja '52 170w

Times [London] Lit Sup p674 O 26 '51 700w

CONTENTS

INTRODUCTION

1851
Survey *Illustrations*

TRANSITION

1951
Survey *Illustrations*

NOTES
AND
ACKNOWLEDGEMENTS

COLOPHON

LIST OF ILLUSTRATIONS

LIST OF ILLUSTRATIONS

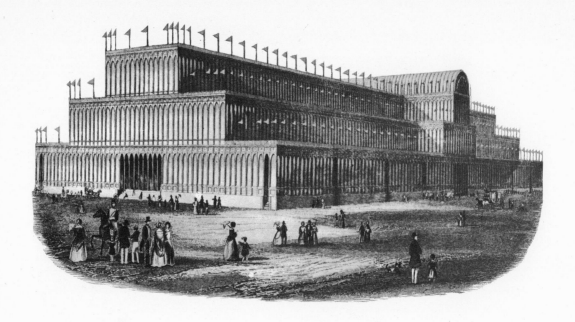

'In every age, and in all countries, printing denotes the state of civilisation. Its products deeply interest all grades of society — contribute to their moral, intellectual and social civilisation, and give activity and employment to so many minds and hands.'

This statement, made by the International Jury of the Class devoted to the paper, stationery, printing and bookbinding trade at the Great Exhibition of 1851, shows that it was considered opportune to draw a clear distinction between the exhibits of this Class, affirming as it does the spiritual and moral values of printing in addition to the physical.

'Printer's Progress 1851–1951' differs in its aims from the various scholarly and practical books systematically surveying the history of printing, or conveying technical knowledge of one or several methods of the printing or allied trades. It was felt that 1951, the year of the Festival of Britain, in commemoration of the Great Exhibition held in London in 1851, would prove a welcome date to draw a comparison between the work and means, and the economic and social standing of the printer of today and of his colleague of a hundred years ago.

It is an attempt to provide those who are interested in the optical and intellectual aspects of the products of printing with faithful replicas of the printed matter of 1851 and with typical illustrations revealing the versatility in design and reproduction media of the printer of our day.

Surveys of the years 1851 and 1951 endeavour to sum up the materials, machinery, reproduction and printing processes, the printer's appreciation of design, and his economic and social background.

The survey of 1851 is an attempt to strike a fair balance between the assessment given in the Jury's report of the printing and allied trades in that year and our assessment of the position of the printer in 1851. Techniques, materials and machinery which, according to the experts of a century ago, seemed unsurpassable, are seen to be mere stages of a continual development.

In displaying the printer's progress of the years 1851 and 1951 side by side, without including the intermediate phases, it is hoped that 'Printer's Progress 1851–1951' will be able to give a clear realisation of both the aesthetic and technical differences. It would be vain to attempt the presentation of such a comparison without drawing attention to the revolutionary changes which the introduction of the camera has brought about in blockmaking, photo-lithography, gravure and photocomposing between these two dates.

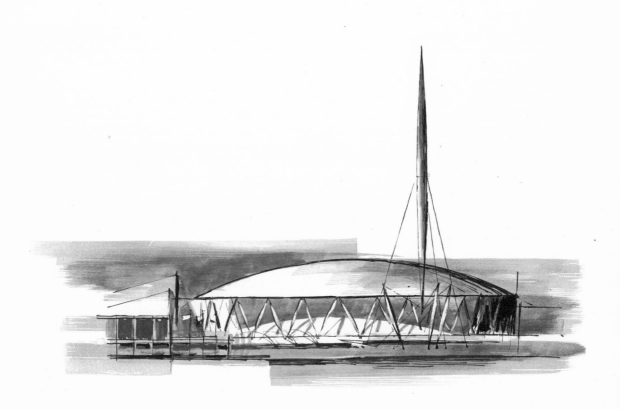

If there had happened to be an exhibition of printing plant in 1800, those who went to see it would have had before their eyes apparatuses and processes which hardly differed from those of 1500. For it was the first half of the nineteenth century that was to see the transformation of printing from a manual craft into a semi-mechanized industry. Any septuagenarian printer who chanced to go to Hyde Park in 1851 would have been quick to realize how completely the whole complexion of the trade, technically, economically and socially, had altered during the previous fifty years.

There was, late in the eighteenth century, only a limited interest in printing and its associated techniques and trades. When the eminent French typefounder, S. P. Fournier *le jeune*, published his *Manuel Typographique* (1764–66) he had at least one eye on a non-professional public, for on the title-page he indicated that his work would be of interest and use to *gens de lettres*. While although Baskerville in Birmingham and Bodoni in Parma were both well accustomed to receiving visits from men of quality and learning, and to showing them round their printing and typefounding establishments, it is doubtful, however, whether the general public had either opportunity or desire to see printers' equipment or printers at work. The printing exhibits at The Great Exhibition, therefore, must have constituted an interesting novelty to the men, women, and children who flocked in their thousands to Hyde Park in 1851; the more so since some machines were manned and actually at work.

The American, Belgian, British, French and German Jurors in charge of the printing exhibits, attempted in their *Report*, signed by three of them in the capacity of Reporters, to evaluate the progress made during the preceding few decades. This document, unfortunately, whilst containing many interesting facts and figures, does not offer that reasoned assessment of the state of printing and its allied trades and crafts in 1851 which would be so useful to us now. Today, at a distance of one hundred years, and with an extensive documentation at our disposal, we can better appreciate the relative importance of many factors which the Reporters were then unable to consider objectively.

Nevertheless, in expressing their hope that the union of all nations gathered together for the Exhibition might hasten the 'peaceful solution of a question which concerns at once the rights of justice, of literature, of the sciences and of typography', they fully acknowledged what an immense spiritual, moral and intellectual influence can be wielded by the printed word.

Historical The *Report* also indicated that there had been a great expansion of the printing trade and its products during the previous fifty years or so. This was true in France, as well as in England, for the effects of the Revolution were great. Until 1789 the number of printing offices permitted to function in France was limited by decree; namely, thirty-six in Paris, and far fewer in individual provincial towns. But this arbitrary limitation was swept away by the Revolution, and an enormous expansion of printing and publishing activity followed.

In England, however, in 1789, there was no artificial limitation of the printing trade; indeed, there had been none since 1695. But the industrial revolution was getting into its stride, and a new, important and energetic middle class required newspapers to keep in touch with the affairs of the world, books for instruction and entertainment, and 'commercial' printing for its business activities. Accordingly, the number of printing offices in London increased from 124 to 216 between 1785 and 1808; by 1826 there were as many as 323 firms trading in the capital; and by the middle of the century their number exceeded 400. The provincial trade, too, was steadily expanding. In this connexion it is not, perhaps, generally realized that no *daily* newspapers were published outside London until 1855, and the real expansion of printing in the provinces did not commence in earnest until after that date.

Printing The equipment used by printers in 1800 was basically the same as that used by their grandfathers in 1700. Indeed, with the exception of minor modifications to the traditional wooden handpress in the middle of the seventeenth century, the tools and technique of letterpress printers were the same in 1800 as they were in 1500. Printing types, laboriously cast by hand at a rate of a few hundred letters per hour, were set up by hand at an average speed of some 1,500 letters per hour for straightforward solid matter.

The wooden handpress, attended by two men (one to ink the forme and to pull the lever, the other to lay on and take off the sheets of paper), was able to produce about 250 impressions in the hour. But, although capable of good work, the wooden press had many defects. There was, for instance, a limit to the size of the platen which could be fitted, which thus made two pulls necessary for large formes, the latter being moved further along under the platen for the second impression. Nor, owing to the material used for the construction of the old presses, could they be made sufficiently rigid; while the impression mechanism, a simple bar actuating a screw, was both primitive in conception and laborious to work.

Many inconclusive experiments were made to improve the wooden handpress at the end of the eighteenth century; but it was not, in fact, until 1799, when Lord Stanhope perfected an iron handpress, with an impression mechanism actuated on a lever principle, that any really important advance was made. The advantages of the Stanhope press, and of many variants made during the following two decades, were: rigidity of construction, comparative ease of operation, and the opportunity of printing, at one pull of the bar, larger sizes of paper than had previously been possible. Up till 1860, when small and cheap cylinder presses and platen machines were within the reach of modest concerns, the iron press was the standard printing equipment for all firms who could not run to the expense of installing flatbed cylinder machines. Moreover, by 1830, when the larger offices were already using steam-driven cylinder presses for bookwork, books which required a really high standard of presswork were still printed on handpresses, the more so if they contained wood-engravings which the customer desired to be printed with care.

The development of the steam-driven flatbed cylinder press, Frederick Koenig's invention, which was first used at *The Times* in 1814, was due to a newspaper proprietor's need to produce a given number of copies of his paper in a limited space of time. The later a morning paper can be sent to press the better, since its columns can thus be kept open for late news. On the other hand, the printing must be completed in time for the journal to be in the hands of its readers no later than competitive sheets. From 1800 onwards, with a rising circulation due to improved news gathering, independence from government political subsidies, and the public's desire for accurate intelligence from the Continental theatres of war, the proprietors of *The Times* had a constant difficulty in printing, in the time available, sufficient copies to meet the demand. The bottleneck was in the press room, where the handpress was only capable of 250 impressions per hour. Recourse was had to duplicate composition for the inner forme, containing the second and the third pages, but this was an expensive procedure. John Walter the second, principal proprietor of *The Times*, was thus prepared to risk a large sum of money in subsidizing and supporting Koenig's invention — which was the prototype of the flatbed cylinder presses in common use today — first, in order to save the expense of duplicate setting; and secondly, so as to be able to print the newspaper quickly; for the Koenig machine was capable of an output of about 1,000 perfected sheets in an hour.

This is the first instance of a newspaper printer sponsoring an invention which was later to be taken up by the general trade. But while it would not be true to say that all subsequent inventions and improvements in printing technique were sponsored in newspaper offices, nevertheless newspaper printers, with their particular requirement of speed of output, made a pioneer use of much plant which was later to be adopted, even if in a modified form, by general and commercial printers. Yet, if by 1820 no more than half-a-dozen cylinder presses were in use in London, and these mostly by newspaper printers, by this date the technical organization of newspaper printing already differed in every respect from that of book printing. It had become a specialized branch of its own.

The wet-flong stereotyping process, too, was first developed in Britain by *The Times* in the middle of the nineteenth century, and later it was *The Times* again which was the first daily to employ mechanical typesetting machinery, namely the Kastenbein typesetter (1868). A New York newspaper printer (1886), however, was to develop the Linotype typesetting machine, and the influence of American newspaper proprietors on the perfection of the halftone engraving process is also important.

The steam-driven cylinder press, too, found its initial use in this country and elsewhere among newspaper printers. But, probably, it was not until about 1830 that this type of machine was much employed for book and general printing, and it was William Clowes who was responsible for the first really large installation of machines. He used them for printing the *Penny Magazine*, the first mass-circulation weekly periodical, which, founded in 1836, soon attained the then unprecedented circulation of 180,000 copies per issue.

But already *The Times* had abandoned its Koenig machines, and was using the first of a series of special-purpose newspaper printing machines, successively capable of producing from 4,000 to 10,000 copies per hour. These culminated in the invention of the Walter Press, the first reel-fed newspaper rotary (1866). Applegath's 9-feeder vertical sheet-fed rotary, designed for *The Times* and installed at Printing House Square in 1848, was shown at the Great Exhibition in 1851, and was one of the greatest attractions of the small printing section (see illustration No. 1). The machine shown at Hyde Park actually was a smaller model, with fewer feeding sections, owned by the

Illustrated London News, but in all other respects was similar to the apparatus in use at Printing House Square.

That *The Times* in 1851 required a machine capable of producing 10,000 impressions per hour was due to the fact that its circulation was then about 38,000. Steadily rising since 1814, when the Koenig machine dealt with an output of 5,000 copies every night, by 1837 its circulation was 9,800, and eight years later had attained 26,000. Eight other London sheets averaged 4,000 copies per day in 1846, but rather less in 1851. *The Times* reigned supreme.

Composing As far as composing is concerned, no important innovations took place during the period 1800 to 1850. There were several attempts during the 1840's to construct typesetting machines, but these early experiments were not successful. The newspaper proprietors, however, showed little or no interest in them, and the general printers saw no reason to take the plunge. While the compositors — who feared a threat to their livelihood, for there was a plentiful supply of cheap labour — were quick to denounce the few machines then in existence as uneconomic in use and mechanically unsound. The time for mechanical composition was not yet ripe.

The steady increase in book and periodical printing which is evident after 1830, coupled with an abundant supply of hands for the composing departments, gave rise to a development in composition methods which was not without its effect on the aesthetics of contemporary printing. This was the companionship system, by which small groups of piece-workers (companionships) collaborated on the setting-up of books and periodicals. Each 'ship' was headed by a clicker (not a foreman) who made-up and imposed the types which had been set — with great expedition and little regard to the niceties of spacing — by the other members of the team. Earnings were shared, the clicker being paid a small additional sum for his trouble in organizing the flow of production and keeping the piece-work accounts of the 'ship'. The low standards of much Victorian printing are entirely due to this system of working.

Type Faces Although a number of typefounders showed their products at the Great Exhibition, there was no informed interest in type design, nor, indeed, in the principles of good book and jobbing typography. There was a marked deterioration in typographical standards after 1820. When considering typography and book production early in the nineteenth century, the tendency is to think first of such able practitioners as Bulmer, Bensley and John Bell. In or about 1800, however, there was at least a score of London printers capable of producing work in which good taste, decent typesetting, and fair standards of presswork were manifested. These men used the traditional 'modern' faces with great effectiveness. But they had at their disposal only a limited range of display types, among which can be counted Fry's Old Face Open, still in the repertory of discriminating printers.

It is not easy to explain why the type designers (who also engraved the punches) of the 1830's and later produced those anaemic looking 'modern' faces which we associate with the printing of the middle of the century. A degree of virtuosity was no doubt required for the cutting of those abruptly graduated thick and thin strokes, and a certain type of craftsman has always allowed virtuosity to get the better of good taste. It may well have been that a fashion for highly calendered paper, used to show wood-engravings to their best advantage, was to some extent responsible for the production of the mid-century 'moderns'. Fine hairlines cannot be effectively printed on a rough-surfaced paper.

In 1800 a comparatively small range of display types was available to printers, and but one or two 'ornamental' designs. Yet by 1850 there was a great choice of display material, including a diversity of those lively and often grotesque designs of Victorian jobbing printing so familiar to the student (see illustrations Nos. 21, 45 and 47). Nevertheless, this mass of display material was not designed and marketed by the typefounders for the sake of 'art', but because there was an expanding demand for types to be used in advertising and jobbing work.

Between 1801 and 1851 there was a rise in the population of Great Britain from 10 million to 20 million. The cost of living on the other hand, which in 1801 was some 50 per cent higher than it was fifty years later, and in 1813, when the Napoleonic wars were approaching their climax, about 80 per cent higher, steadily decreased from 1815 onwards. Meantime, wages remained fairly stable. The consequent rapid expansion in the production of consumer goods called for more energetic efforts in order to sell them. Hence the demand for display types suitable for forceful and unsophisticated advertising directed towards new and ever greater markets (see illustration No. 45).

Design Appreciation If today much Victorian printing appears to us to be slovenly and ill-planned, it is due, no doubt, to the fact that earlier and better traditions of craftsmanship had been forgotten. The few printers and publishers who were asked to produce something 'different' or 'better' were content to fall back upon the old-face types of Caslon and other eighteenth-century punchcutters, and to design what we know as 'period' printing. It had not yet occurred to anyone, least of all to master printers, that typography and type design were subjects worthy of any critical attention and analysis. By 'fine printing' they meant presswork of a high standard, especially in connexion with books illustrated with engravings on wood.

Illustration Techniques and Processes The 'trade' wood-engravers were an important feature of the nineteenth-century printing industry. Thomas Bewick (1753–1828) had revolutionized the technique of wood-engraving by working on the end of the grain of the wood, instead of along the grain, and with a burin instead of a knife, and had given the art a great new impetus. He was, indeed, the founder of that school of engravers whose finest work is to be seen in the illustrated books of the 1860's. These men were more than successful interpreters of the drawings of the eminent illustrators for whom they worked; many of them were creative artists in their own right. An examination of engravings by the brothers Dalziel (see illustration No. III) will soon prove the truth of this statement. But besides the artist-engravers there was a host of capable craftsmen whose work is more or less forgotten today, as well as many hacks; and it was these engravers who produced the many blocks required by jobbing printers and their customers to illustrate an increasingly wide range of printed matter (see illustrations Nos. 1, 16, 17, 35, 40, 43, 45 and 46).

There was, too, a new race of practitioners in various specialities, such as die-cutting, recess engraving for postage stamps and securities, 'patent' illustration processes, etc. The *Report of the Juries* mentions a whole host of these graphic 'specialities': Branston and Vizetelli's lottery tickets printed in several colours, Whitling's 'security' engravings — in which the 'rose' machine invented by Sir William Congreve played an important part — and Baxter's colour prints amongst them. The *Report* also describes a great variety of experimental graphic processes, many of them developed by the Imperial Printing Office at Vienna, which had as their object the manufacture or multiplication of printing surfaces by chemical means (see 'Technical Data, 1851'). Many of these tentative experiments, however, had little — if any — commercial application, and they were mostly forgotten when the possibilities of photo-mechanical processes were realized and exploited, for the potentialities contained in the application of the camera to the manufacture of printing surfaces were not known in 1851.

Lithography The *Report* has very little to say on the subject of lithography. Senefelder's invention was introduced to England in 1800 by the inventor himself, but it is Rudolf Ackermann, who started his Lithographic Press in London in 1817, who may be regarded as the real popularizer of lithography in Britain. It took a long time, however, for the multi-colour process to displace original black-and-tint work or even the ordinary black-and-white print. Actually the greater part of press colour lithography work in the 1830's and 1840's is of the black-and-tint type, the lemon or salmon-coloured ground being almost a distinctive feature of this period. Hand-coloured lithographs are even more common, this method being often employed on prints of the black-and-tint species.

It is not surprising that printers were slow in embarking on the installation of expensive machinery and on the training of craftsmen needed for multi-colour lithographic work, once it is realized that the wages of those employed on hand-colouring did not exceed four or five shillings for a six-day week of ten hours' daily work. In establishments producing Valentines and greeting cards, up to a hundred or more persons were to be found working on hand-colouring, each one only dealing with a specific part and working in only one colour.

The first widespread commercial application of colour lithography can be associated with Thomas de la Rue, a member of the well-known London printing firm, who, in 1832, patented a process of printing playing cards in oil colours by lithography in place of the old method of stencilling them. But it appears that he was more interested in the production of playing cards than in the general development of colour lithography.

The real pioneer in the publication of chromolithography was Owen Jones, who began printing coloured illustrations of his *Plans, Sections and Details of the Alhambra* in March 1836, a superbly produced book, many of its plates showing the ornamental designs of the Alhambra in six colours and gold, and one of them even being embossed. The earliest date on any plate in this work is 1837, but the date on the title page is 1842. Prior to this, under the imprint of M. & N. Hanhart, Lithographic Printers, London, a Music Album was published, entitled *The Queen's Boudoir*, the preface to which is dated London 1st November 1840, the frontispiece drawn on stone by J. Brandard in red, black and ochre, and the title page executed in black, yellow, red, blue and gold. The publishers, Jefferys and Nelson, of 21 Soho Square, claim in their introduction that the illustrations in chromolithography are specimens of an art first used in connexion with music by the Proprietors of *The Queen's Boudoir*.

Bookbinding In their review of the bookbinding exhibits, the Jurors failed to appreciate the economic importance of mass-produced cloth bindings, of which a few were on view (see illustrations Nos. 8c and 12), and appear to have been mainly interested in the *chefs d'œuvre* exhibited by leather binders both from this country and from abroad. Yet the cloth binding case, first developed about 1825, was cheaper and easier to produce than one in leather executed in the traditional manner, and more durable than a covering of boards lined with paper. It was, too, an essential feature of the mid-century 'cheap-book', printed by machine on paper made by machine.

Paper Machine-made paper, too, was a comparatively recent invention. Originally made in France by Nicholas Louis Robart, it was perfected in that country by François Didot during the last decade of the eighteenth century. The short-lived Peace of Amiens (1802) gave Didot an opportunity of visiting England, where he sold patent rights to the Fourdrinier brothers. By 1851 there were 413 paper-making machines at work in this country, producing an annual tonnage of 62,960 tons.

In 1837 the labour cost of manning one vat for the production of hand-made paper was £6 per week, but that for a machine which could produce between five and seven times as much paper in the same time, was only £4 10s. In reading the *Report of the Select-Committee on Fourdrinier's Patent* (1837), it can readily be realized that the men who gave evidence were well aware of the economic importance of two inventions which had been developed in their own lifetimes: the paper-making machine and the printing machine.

Publishing The combination of cheap materials and speedy printing enabled publishers to order large editions of some books and drastically to reduce the selling prices. Thus a novelist of the standing of Sir Walter Scott was able to put on the market an edition of his own works at the low price of 5s per volume instead of the previous 16s, thereby creating such a demand that 1,000 volumes had to be produced daily. The British and Foreign Bible Society, too, was able to announce during the opening month of the Great Exhibition, that since its foundation in 1804 more than 24,000,000 copies of the Testaments, printed in as many as 165 different languages, had been distributed over the face of the globe, while publications issued by the University Presses of Oxford and Cambridge gained equally wide distribution.

In London, the centre of the book trade, nearly 3,000 works — including new editions — were published annually, their total value amounting to some £450,000, while the sale of as many as 230 monthly and quarterly magazines yielded a further half a million pounds.

The new mass-circulation weeklies, such as the *Penny Magazine* (1836) and *Illustrated London News* (1842), also resulted from the new methods of mass production and the demand for good and inexpensive reading matter from a new reading public.

Envelopes The introduction of Penny Postage in 1839 exercised another tremendous effect on the papermaking industry, for the number of letters delivered in the United Kingdom rose from 76 million in 1839 to 360 million in 1851. Whereas, too, in 1839, a quire of cheap writing paper cost 6d, by 1851 the same amount of paper could be bought for $2\frac{1}{2}$d, and contained in a neat and convenient packet, instead of being sold loose. As for envelopes, although they had long been in common use in France, very little progress was made with their manufacture in Great Britain before the invention, in 1845, of De La Rue's patent envelope-making machine, one of which actually at work was to prove a great attraction at the Exhibition. The revolutionary effects of this machine can be judged by the suggestion in the *Report* that by 1847 the annual domestic consumption of envelopes had reached 300 million. Concurrently, the manufacture of fancy stationery and papers introduced a fresh outlet to a thriving industry.

Printing: Social and Economic By 1800 the Stationers' Company, with a membership of some 400 (twice as large as in 1700), had completely lost its old importance and powers of disciplinary regulation of the trade. It was no more than a society of employers in the printing, bookselling and stationery trades who made their membership of the Livery an excuse for periodical conviviality. But there was already in existence an Association of London Master Printers, formed solely to resist successive wage claims from the compositors and pressmen. Yet of the 216 London firms known to have existed in 1808, and of the 323 who were working in 1826, the majority were very modest concerns, few employing more than half-a-dozen hands. Such was still the position in 1855, when the London Society of Compositors published a list of 423 offices, for only four firms employed more than one hundred compositors: Messrs Clowes, book-printers; the Spottiswoodes, book and parliamentary printers; the Hansards, specialists in parliamentary work; and Messrs Savill & Edwards, who are no longer in business. One firm, Bradbury & Agnew, then as now the printers of *Punch* (see illustration No. 17), had between eighty and ninety men; six other houses employed between fifty and sixty hands in their composing rooms; and there were some fourteen offices with between thirty and forty compositors. But from an over-all survey it would appear that out of the total of 423 printing shops, as many as 288 employed less than three compositors, and that not more than three dozen had composing-room staffs of over twenty. The conclusion to be drawn is that although in 1855 the London trade was three and a half times larger than in 1785, the investment in expensive plant and equipment was mainly confined to a small and powerful group of firms. The average London master printer in 1851 was, therefore, a tradesman in a modest way of business rather than an industrialist. Nor is there any reason to believe that the provincial trade was at this time of any great importance.

In addition to the emergence and growing importance of the new commercial middle class there were, too, stirrings from the proletariat. As has been said, before the middle of the eighteenth century, printing firms were without exception modest concerns, employing very few workmen. But the appearance after 1750 of a few businesses very much larger in size and importance than any that had existed before, created conditions favourable to trade union activity. Where sizable bodies of workmen were gathered together under one roof but, owing to changing economic conditions, with little hope of rising into the ranks of the employers, there was a tendency to combine or organize for the mutual protection and betterment of conditions of employment. The first evidence of such combination, or trade union activity in the modern sense of the word, is contained in an agreement, dated 1785, between London compositors and a group of employers. Thus, the London compositors were in the vanguard of the Trade Union movement.

By 1810 the union was firmly established, but it foundered in 1816, immediately after the end of the Napoleonic wars. The cost of living, which had been rising for the past fifteen years, then steeply declined, and in a period of slump following a long commercial and industrial boom, the printing trade union movement lost ground. The compositors, however, re-established their society in 1817, and the newspaper-compositors founded their own special section in 1820. The London pressmen, too, had their own society. The compositors, traditionally the 'activists' of the printing trade, were not much in evidence during the 1820's, but were energetic in recruiting members and negotiating improved conditions of employment during the 1830's. The rise of the provincial unions can be dated from 1840. Attempts to merge the London and provincial unions failed in 1846, and in 1848 the London union was both bankrupt and again at the point of dissolution. Reformed once more in the same year, by 1851 its affairs were in good order, and at the time of the Great Exhibition, trade unionism was an accepted factor in the British printing trade. Whilst the London unions did not wield great power, they were, nevertheless, an integral part of a trade in which specialization and mechanization were playing an increasingly important part.

There were, in 1851, some 8,500 journeymen and 6,000 apprentices employed in the printing trade in the British Isles. Out of this total, 3,130 men and 2,300 boys were engaged in newspaper work; 4,900 men and 3,700 boys in jobbing, bookwork and publications; and 460 men in the London daily press, where boy labour was not countenanced. Between them these 8,500 men earned £8,725 weekly, wages in London ranging from 33s to 48s; in England and Wales from 18s to 30s; in Ireland from 12s to 32s 6d; and in Scotland from 20s to 25s.

The Printer's Progress The growth of the British railway system affected every department of this country's economy after 1830. In the latter year the length of track operated was only about 97 miles; yet in 1840 the total mileage open had increased to nearly 1,500; and by the middle of the century 6,560 miles of railway had been built. By 1851 most of the principal manufacturing towns and regional centres in England had rail connexion with London, although cross-country lines had yet to be developed.

This expansion was not without its impact on the British printing and allied trades. For it was cheaper and easier not only to move raw materials in bulk (i.e. paper), but also to bring the industry's finished products — newspapers, books, etc — quickly from London, which was still their principal manufacturing centre in 1851, to the rapidly expanding outlying markets. The provincial printing trade could have no great industrial importance until after the railways were built, nor did the provincial newspaper press achieve any great economic influence or social importance until after 1855, when the Newspaper Stamp Tax of one penny was repealed. It should be recalled that until that year no daily newspaper was published in England outside London.

Printing in 1851, the year of the Great Exhibition, was at the crossroads. During the preceding fifty years it had been transformed from a manual craft into a mechanized industry, although there were still a great many small and badly equipped shops. Already there were the first signs of specialization, which is the feature of the printing trade today. Newspaper and periodical printing were already profitable specialities, even if they did require large and expensive plant. A number of firms, too, were beginning to specialize in railway work (see illustration No. 48), books, or colour printing.

Mechanization was on its way. But it was not until 1886 that the first Mergenthaler Linotype typesetting machine was set to work at *The New York Tribune*, thus firmly establishing mechanical composition for the first time. This was, however, preceded by the establishment of the photo-mechanical processes in 1882.

Queen Victoria and the Prince Consort viewing printing presses at the Great Exhibition.

THE JOURNAL

OF

THE GREAT EXHIBITION

OF

1851.

ITS ORIGIN, HISTORY, AND PROGRESS.

––––––––

LONDON:

JOHN CROCKFORD,—THE CRITIC, LONDON LITERARY JOURNAL OFFICE,
29, ESSEX STREET, STRAND.

1851.

By Authority of the Royal Commission.

OFFICIAL CATALOGUE

OF THE

GREAT EXHIBITION

OF THE

WORKS OF INDUSTRY OF ALL NATIONS,

1851.

THE EARTH IS THE LORD'S, AND ALL THAT THEREIN IS:
THE COMPASS OF THE WORLD AND THEY THAT DWELL THEREIN.

FOURTH CORRECTED AND IMPROVED EDITION, 15th September, 1851.

LONDON:
SPICER BROTHERS, WHOLESALE STATIONERS; W. CLOWES & SONS, PRINTERS;
Contractors to the Royal Commission,
29 NEW BRIDGE STREET, BLACKFRIARS, AND AT THE EXHIBITION BUILDING, HYDE PARK.

3

SEASON TICKET OF ADMISSION
To the Exhibition of the Works of Industry
OF ALL NATIONS 1851.
No 1

Class 17. PAPER, PRINTING, AND BOOKBINDING.

—— Areas F. 27 to 29; G. H. I. J. 26, 27. ——

1 ACKERMAN & Co. 96 Strand.—Envelope case. Sea weeds. Pole screens. Ornamental colour box. Scrap book.

4 HUGHES, E. Greenwich Hospital Schools, Des.—An improved map of the British islands, physical, political, and industrial. Map of Palestine and adjacent countries.

5 REMNANT, EDMONDS, & REMNANT, 9 Lovell's Ct. Paternoster Row.—Specimens of binding in morocco, vellum, Russia, and calf, elegant, plain, and antique. Sheep and cloth, plain and elegant.

7 HAWTHORNE, J. 77 Charrington St. Manu.—Various descriptions of writing inks, and the materials from which they are made. Specimens of hair dyeing with ink. Nutgalls, fruit of the Terminalia Chebula, from Bengal. Inks.

8 EVANS, J. S. 64 Berwick St. Soho, Manu.—Bookbinding; and leather stained in imitation of woods.

9 FAIRBAIRN, R. 37 Gt. Cambridge St. Hackney Rd. Manu.—Specimens of wood type for printing, &c.

10 FISHER, J. H. New North Rd. Hoxton, Inv.—Specimen of bank note printed in chemical water-colour, in two colours at one operation.

11 GALLARD, W. 30 Lisson Grove, Des.—Portable frame for cases at the imposing stone, or for extra cases.

12 GILL, T. D. 27 Charlotte St. Fitzroy Sq. Inv.—Postage stamp expedient, for saving time, &c.

14 BINNS & GOODWIN, Bath. — Treatise on British grasses with natural illustrations.

17 HIDER, ELIZABETH, 15 Manor Pl. King's Road, Chelsea, Des. and Manu.—Fancy floral paper for valentines.

18 DEAN & SON, 35 Threadneedle St.—Ornamented and illustrated letter and note paper.

19 STIDOLPH, —, 2 New Bond St., Bath, Inv.—" The Chiragon," or hand-guide for blind and tremulous writers.

20 HUGHES, G. A. 9 Mount Row, Westminster Rd. Inv. (Blind)—Machines for enabling the blind to write, calculate, and copy music, &c.

21 HYDE & Co. 61 Fleet St. Manu.—Rider's new mode of taking impressions from intaglios. Solid India and other sealing-wax.

22 KING, T. & J. H. 4 Bartlett's Buildings, Holborn Hill, Des. and Manu.—Specimen of a new type-music. Original design of a series of letters called arabesques.

23 KIRBY, J. 103 Cornwall Rd. Lambeth.—Split paper, and improved method of mounting woodcuts.

24 LEIGHTON, J. & J. 40 Brewer St. Golden Sq.—Specimens of bookbinding and processes, designs by Luke Limner. Imitations of old printing, &c.

25 LLOYD, R. 26 Birchin Lane, Inv. Pat. and Manu.—Cork cut by machinery, to preserve books and paintings from damp.

26 MACOMIE & Co. 6 Percy St. Bedford Sq. Manu.—Specimens of pulpit, family Bible, and other binding. A clock case.

27 MANSELL, J. 35 Red Lion Sq. Des. and Manu.—Ornaments for decorating linens, cloths, &c. Embossed and perforated Bristol boards. Paper. Envelopes and cards, &c.

29 MARTIN, J. Pat.—Waterproof paper. The paper manufactured by Mr. Pearson, Branthwaite.

31 PARSONS, FLETCHER, & Co. 22 Bread St. Manu.—Printers' inks, black and coloured.

32 PENNY, H. 11 Old Bailey, Manu.—Metallic pocket-books.

33 PINCHES & Co. 27 Oxendon St. Manu.—Illuminated note paper. Stamping in relief. Smith's improved stamping press. Medal, button, and other dies.

34 ROYSTON & BROWN, 40 & 41 Old Broad St. Manu.—Specimens of bank notes and bills of exchange, engraved by a patent process to prevent forgery. Various account books.

35 SAFSFORD, N. 17 Kirby St. Hatton Garden, Manu.—Specimen of bookbinding.

36 SAUNDERS, T. H. Queenhithe, and Dartford, Kent, Manu.—Parchment paper. Bank-note papers. Glass transparency to show the water mark. Safety paper for cheques, &c.

37 SAUNDERSON, C. Kilburn Lodge. Kilburn, Prop.—Map of Ireland, by J. Dower.

38 SCHLESINGER & Co. 8 Old Jewry—Registered metallic memorandum books. Pocket-books. Letter-clips. Parallel rulers.

40 SILVERLOCK, H. 3 Wardrobe Ter. Doctors' Commons, Des.—Letterpress printing from stereotype plates of medallion and machine engraving.

41 SMITH, J. 42 Rathbone Pl. Inv. and Manu.—Adhesive envelopes. &c. Dowse's tracing and writing cloth.

42 SPICER BROTHERS, New Bridge St. London, Wholesale and Export Stationers, Prop.—Writing papers, Joynson's extra superfine quality. Large bank post. Imperial, royal, and demy. Foolscap, for account books. Superfine plate papers for engravings and lithograph printing. Superfine printing papers. Fine news. Fine long elephant, in a sheet of 750 yards in length. Fine double long elephant, in one sheet 46 inches wide and 2,500 yards in length, for paper staining, &c. Long elephant, for paper hangings. Brown papers from pure rope, very tough for packing. A sheet of brown paper, 93 inches wide, 420 feet long. Millboards, for bookbinding, &c.

42A JOYNSON, W. St. Mary Cray, Manu.—Specimens of writing paper. Large bank post, blue wove, blue laid, and cream laid post; cream laid and blue laid foolscap.

43 TARRANT, A. 190 High Holborn, Manu.—Specimens of bookbinding.

44 THOMAS & SONS, 20 Cornhill, Manu.—Ledgers in various sizes and bindings.

45 TURNBULL, J. L. & J. Holywell Mount, Shoreditch, Manu.—London drawing boards. Royal drawing boards. Coloured crayon boards, &c.

46 WATERLOW & SONS, 66 London Wall, Manu.—Account books, with patent backs, and general stationery.

47 WEDGWOOD, R. 84 Lombard St. Manu.—Patent manifold writer. Improved noctograph for the blind, &c. Registered desk clip.

48 WESTLEY, J. Playhouse Yard, Blackfriars—Specimens of bookbinding by hand and by machinery. Designs by Luke Limner.

49 WHITAKER, R. 13 & 14 Little Britain—Playing-cards, the backs ornamented in gold and colours.

51 WHITEMAN, F. J. 19 Little Queen St. Holborn, Manu.—Improved perforated plates for marking linen, &c. (In North Gallery, F. 18.)

52 WIDNALL, G. F. 6 Harrow Rd. Paddington, Inv.—Railway, omnibus, and toll-bar pocket-book and purse.

53 WILLIAMS, J. 29 Bucklersbury, Manu.—An assortment of ledgers.

55 ARLISS & TUCKER, 15 Frith St. Soho, Inv. and Manu.—Views of the Exhibition Building. printed on tinfoil, &c.

58 ATKINSON, W. Lambs' Passage, Finsbury, Manu.—Dyed and embossed calico, for bookbinding purposes.

No.	Name and Address of Exhibitor and London Agent, Description of Article, &c.	Price.

£. s. d.

Class 16—*continued*.

No. 3. Patent moveable panel light hunting saddle, complete . . . . — 4 4 0

No. 4. Patent moveable panel stout agricultural saddle, complete for durability and economy 4 4 0

No. 5. Portable self-acting shade for harness bridles, to prevent horses shying . . 0 16 6

No. 6. Registered Pelham bridle, complete 1 11 6

No. 7. Registered Weymouth bridle, complete 1 8 6

No. 8. Body roller, with an improved buckle and shap 0 10 6

No. 9. Suit of horse clothing, complete . . 4 4 0

Nos. 10, 11. A variety of patterns of webs for girths, roller, brace, riding belts, and registered bindings.

No. 12. Samples of webs.

N.B. Articles Nos. 3, 4, and 5 were highly commended by the Judges' Report of the Royal Agricultural Society's Meeting at Shrewsbury.

Class 17. Paper, Printing, and Bookbinding.

7 HAWTHORNE, JAMES, 77, *Charrington Street.*

Blue, black, and blue ink which turns black, 3 half-pint bottles for 0 1 0

Hair dye . . . . per bottle 0 1 6

Ink for staining oak and mahogany, per gall. 0 4 0

169 A HYMN FOR ALL NATIONS, 1851, by M. F. TUPPER, D.C.L., F.R.S., author of " Proverbial Philosophy." Translated into 30 languages (upwards of 50 versions). The Music composed expressly by S. SEBASTIAN WESLEY, Mus. Doc.—London: Printed by THOMAS BRETTELL, *Rupert Street, Haymarket,* and sold by THOMAS HATCHARD, 187, *Piccadilly,* and all booksellers . . . price 0 3 0

192 WHITBREAD, 142, *Oxford Street.*

Map of London, in sheet, plain 0 0 6

Ditto, in cloth case, plain, with index 0 1 0

Ditto, in cloth case, coloured, with index 0 1 6

Ditto, in cloth case, coloured and mounted 0 2 6

Class 18. Woven, Felted, and Laid Fabrics, Dyed and Printed.

19 RICHARD WALFORD, 27, *Lawrence Lane, Cheapside.*

East India silks printed in England.
Prices from . . . . per piece 14/ a 20/

No.	Name and Address of Exhibitor and London Agent, Description of Article, &c.	Price.

£. s. d.

Class 19. Tapestry, Floor Cloths, Lace, and Embroidery.

95 R. Y. BARNES, Manufacturer, *City Road, London.*

Decorative Floor Cloths.

1. 36 feet by 12 feet=48 square yards, at 8/ 19 4 0
2. 12 feet by 12 feet=16 ,, at 8/ 6 8 0
3. 12 feet by 12 feet=16 ,, at 6/ 4 16 0

198 MRS. F. S. HAYTER, 16, *English Street, Hull,* Des. and Manu.

A carpet of Berlin wool, about 14 feet by 15 feet, having taken the manufacturer eight years to complete . . . . . price 150 0 0

401 BRIGHT & CO., Carpet Manufacturers, *Rochdale, London, and Manchester,* JOSH. BURCH & CO., *Carpet Print Works, Crag, near Macclesfield*—Copartners.

Velvet pile carpets, same as exhibited, from . . . . per yard 4/6 a 5/6

Brussels, in super, best, and stout qualities, from . . . . . . per yard 2/10 a 4/

Velvet and terry tapestry fabrics for window draperies, furniture coverings, &c. p. yard 6/ a 9/

Sold wholesale at 20, Skinner Street, Snow Hill, London, and 22, New Brown Street, Manchester.

These goods are woven by Sevier's power loom, and printed by patent machinery, invented by Mr. Burch, the exhibitor.

Class 20. Articles of Clothing, for Immediate, Personal, or Domestic Use.

196 A GREAT OBJECT OBTAINED for the protection to Merchants in shipping coloured and black kid gloves to any part of the world, with a guarantee not to spot. Manufactured by Messrs. J. and J. CORRY, Queen Camel, Somerset, from 6s. to 36s. per dozen.

Class 22. General Hardware, including Locks and Grates.

226 HAGUE, SAMUEL, Cutler, *Eldon Street, Devonshire Lane, Sheffield.*

A case of 63 penknives, with a variety of blades; silver pencils, &c.

No.	per doz. £. s. d.	No.	per doz. £. s. d.	No.	per doz. £. s. d.
1	0 8 0	10	0 8 0	19	1 8 0
2	0 8 0	11	0 11 0	20	0 12 0
3	0 9 0	12	0 12 0	21	1 0 0
4	0 9 0	13	0 11 0	22	1 0 0
5	0 10 6	14	0 12 0	23	1 0 0
6	0 7 6	15	0 14 0	24	0 15 0
7	0 9 0	16	0 15 0	25	0 16 0
8	0 10 0	17	0 9 0	26	0 16 0
9	0 11 0	18	1 5 0	27	0 18 0

5

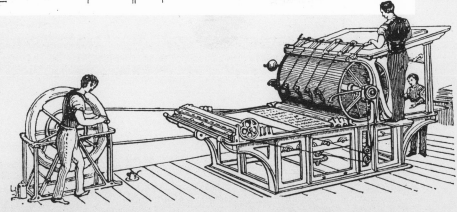

GILBERT'S
POPULAR NARRATIVE
OF THE
GREAT EXHIBITION.

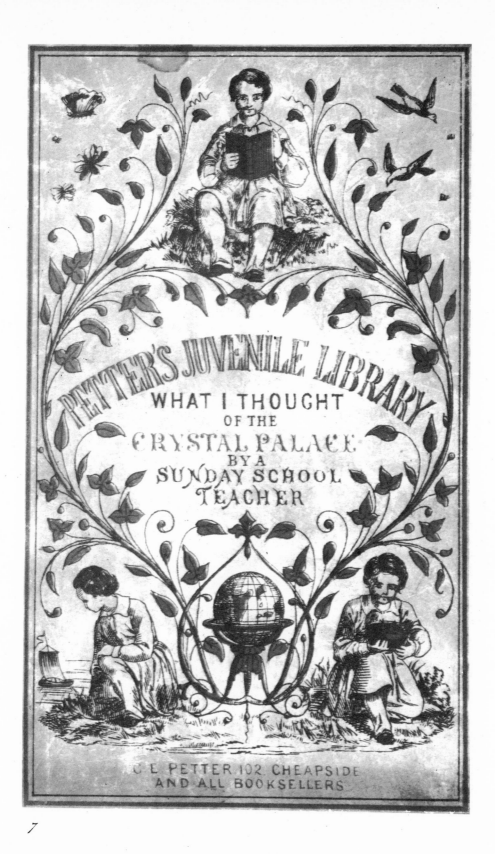

PETTER'S JUVENILE LIBRARY

WHAT I THOUGHT
OF THE
CRYSTAL PALACE
BY A
SUNDAY SCHOOL
TEACHER

J. E. PETTER 102 CHEAPSIDE
AND ALL BOOKSELLERS

7

THE GREAT

EXHIBITION

PRIZE ESSAY

BY THE

REV. J. C. WHISH. M.A.

ADJUDICATORS

REV. RICHARD MICHELL. B.D.

REV. ROBERT WALKER. M.A.

DONOR

REV. J. A. EMERTON. D.D.

LONDON.

LONGMAN, BROWN, GREEN, & LONGMANS.

8

THE HOUSE

THAT

PAXTON BUILT.

A NEW STORY ON AN OLD MODEL.

LONDON:

DARTON AND CO., HOLBORN HILL.

PRICE SIXPENCE, COLOURED.

Here is the Horse Guards, with a party of soldiers on horseback passing under the gateway. It is the great office for all affairs about war, and is one of the most important buildings in England. At its back is St. James's Park.

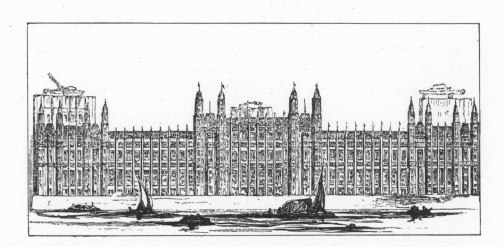

Here are the New Houses of Parliament, which run for a long distance along the River Thames. They are very magnificent; and the Victoria Tower, which you see is not yet completed, will be of an immense height. In these houses, the chief lords and gentlemen of England meet and make laws for the affairs of the country.

6

ever, to suppose that the apparent marble slabs were in any way allied to that mineral, indeed the great difficulty attending the adaptation of the material for the adornment of large surfaces, is the impossibility of cutting it into any thing like superficial extent. The pieces, which are thus used, after being cut, are cemented on to strong iron frames, care being taken that the "rose," as it is called, or pattern of the two seperated pieces should be placed in juxta-position with each other or inequality of design would be the consequence. The Russian candlelabra, ornamented the main avenue, eastward of the great bell.

DENMARK and SWEDEN, not far from the Zollverein department on the south. In the Denmark portion was a curious sample of what was called *Stylography*, which appeared to be a modification of the English process of Glyphography, a means of printing a Copper-plate with Letter-press, the earliest samples of which, we believe, was really first exhibited some years ago in England, in the columns of the *Hereford Times* newspaper; the inventor as is the common lot of the class, living to see others reap the benefit of his perfection of that which Germany had been emulous for years.

Thus clearing our way we have the recollections of the American departments to revel in, without obstruction. Taking the remaining portion of the main avenue, the great attraction the Greek

8d

REMEMBRANCES OF THE GREAT EXHIBITION,

A SERIES OF VIEWS,

Beautifully Engraved on Steel,

FROM

DRAWINGS MADE ON THE SPOT,

Including a general History of its

ORIGIN, PROGRESS & CLOSE.

PRICE 8/6 PLAIN, 14/6 COLOURED.

9

Sculpture
from the
Great Exhibition
OF "1851."
Lithographed by
LOUISA CORBAUX.

LONDON PRINTED & PUB^D BY STANNARD & DIXON, 7, POLAND ST
& ACKERMANN & C^O 96, STRAND

Gratitude.

11

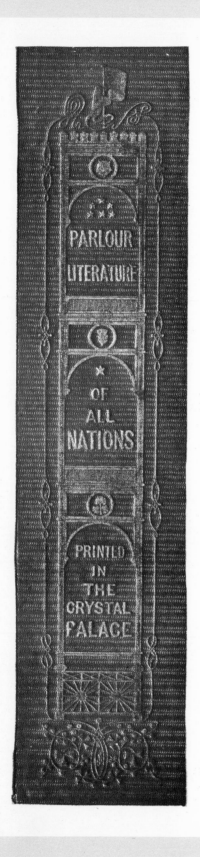

THE
PARLOUR MAGAZINE
OF THE
Literature of
ALL NATIONS.

LONDON:
HOULSTON & STONEMAN

This Volume of the PARLOUR LITERATURE OF ALL NATIONS, was PRINTED IN THE CRYSTAL PALACE, at Machines 158 and 161. The Binding is a new invention by Messrs. LEIGHTON, SON, AND HODGE, of Shoe-lane; entered in the Exhibition, Class 17. The importance of the invention consists in the preservation of the colour of the silver, which had never previously been accomplished.

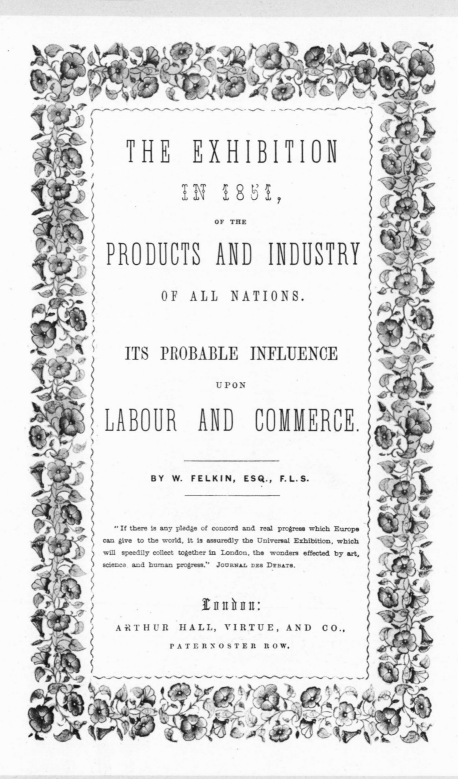

THE EXHIBITION

IN 1851,

OF THE

PRODUCTS AND INDUSTRY

OF ALL NATIONS.

ITS PROBABLE INFLUENCE

UPON

LABOUR AND COMMERCE.

BY W. FELKIN, ESQ., F.L.S.

"If there is any pledge of concord and real progress which Europe can give to the world, it is assuredly the Universal Exhibition, which will speedily collect together in London, the wonders effected by art, science and human progress." JOURNAL DES DEBATS.

London:

ARTHUR HALL, VIRTUE, AND CO.,

PATERNOSTER ROW.

THE TYPOGRAPHICAL PROTECTION CIRCULAR.

PUBLISHED ON THE FIRST DAY OF EVERY MONTH.

No. 25.]   JANUARY, 1851.   [Price One Penny.

THE DISEASE AND THE REMEDY.
(*Concluded from page* 111.)

Another of the great evils—perhaps the greatest—characteristic of strikes, is the *rashness* with which they are entered into. By rashness I do not mean hurry, but rather a want of the requisite reflection preliminary to engaging in them. Dublin and Edinburgh stand prominently forward as evidencing marks of folly in this respect. In all cases, previous to venturing on such a struggle, the projectors of a strike should fairly sum up the elements of power which are in the possession of the belligerent parties; and deduce correct conclusions from the promises thus ascertained. In nine cases out of ten, they will find that the employers are in possession of social, political, and physical power; that they are, in fact, as capitalists, the governors of society, with a sufficiency of tact, intellectual light, and moral unity, to direct them to a concentration of these powers to the accomplishment of a common end for their days; while on the other hand, the workmen are not only destitute of all these essentials to success, but have also to contend against a "floating mass of dormant labour," which is, of itself, more than sufficient to paralyze all attempts at even temporary success, in a contest with parties so unequally matched. While there are fourteen individuals in the labour market, and barely sufficient work for a dozen, it needs no prophecy to foretel how such attempts will end; defeat in future, as in the past, is certain; for the employers, ever alive to their own interests, however much the men may disregard *theirs*—are perfectly cognizant of the "floating mass of dormant labour," and are not slow to perceive the vast power it gives them over the employed. They quietly, but carefully, note the number of tramps passing through the town—look askance at their tattered garments, and draw their inferences accordingly.

No doubt it was from observations similar to these that a proprietor of a certain *journal* in one of the Midland counties, some time since, after making certain calculations, arrived at the conclusion that he was paying higher wages than there was any occasion to do; and, having demonstrated this fact beyond a doubt to his overseer, and suddenly discovered that the paper was not paying so well as formerly, he, on the following Saturday, astonished the hands employed by intimating his intention to *reduce* the prices paid *one half-penny per thousand*, although they were then receiving 7*d.* Nonpariel, 6½*d.* Minion, and 6*d.* Brevier. Of course the men remonstrated against such an unjustifiable reduction, and refused to accede to such terms until they had maturely considered them. The employer dismissed them with the consolatory remark, that each one who did not accept those terms was to consider himself under notice. He stated that he could get double the number of men he wanted at a few hours' notice. The result of all this was, that although the town has always been a staunch supporter of unions, and is at present a prominent branch of the Provincial Typographical Association, the members came to the conclusion to *submit to the reduction*, rather than risk the loss of their situations, and see their frames filled with a beggarly hoard of *rats*. They *knew* their *weakness*, so also did their *employer ;* and if to retreat in time, when there is not the slightest possibility of success, is to be branded as an act of cowardice, then must we look upon England's greatest hero, Lord Wellington, as a coward of no mean degree. " Discretion " in this case was emphatically " the better part of valour." Besides, as a warning beacon to these men, a previous strike, which occurred in another newspaper office in the same town, stood prominently forward,—a heavy and unanswerable proof of the folly of those engaged in it. And, if it were necessary to add to the already numerous facts I have adduced, the utter futility of strikes consummate the end in view. I need only direct the reader's attention, in a few words, to the *results* of the strike here mentioned. It occurred during the time that the Amalgamation was in the zenith of its power, and arose out of the old grievance—the apprentice restriction. There were seven men engaged on this paper, five of whom *struck*, but the other two refusing to do so, were retained, and one of them, a "canny Scot," was made overseer. The end of all this was, that the requisite number of *rats* to replace the *fair* men was easily enough obtained ; and whilst the fair victims—fair and honourable men—were sent upon the road, to shift for themselves as they best might, the *rats* were *secured* in their situations by the office being immediately closed. It has remained closed to this day—more than three years since the strike—the proprietor not only retaining the number of boys which formed the subject matter of dispute, but has since considerably *added* to that number ; which probably would not have been the case had no strike taken place. This town (I purposely withhold its name, as the proceedings relative to the late reduction have not yet been published), previous to the above office being closed, had neither an unfair house nor an unfair man in it ; now I perceive from the last Report of the Provincial Typographical Association, it contains no less than five or six unfair houses—

while the society and non-society men are in equal proportion. Who shall say, after reading this, that strikes, in any case, are beneficial either to the individuals or the trade at large * ?

The last objection (considered by some the most important) to which I shall direct attention is, that so far from strikes tending in any way to decrease boy-labour, they, on the contrary, considerably aggravate the evil. They are pregnant with good only to those natural curiosities in the history of man, known by the cognomen of *rats.* To these animals they are indeed " meat and drink," and in every instance they are hailed by them with the most lively demonstrations, significant of the interest they take in such matters. It is an ascertained fact, that these *rats* consist chiefly of the ignorant and unskilled, whose incapacity and bungling are sufficiently evident to their employer, but who is compelled to put up with the annoyance, seeing that he cannot get *fair* men, his office being closed to individuals of that description. Placed in this "fix," the employer, finding that his office is stocked with men that are any thing but expert at their business—some of them probably, in addition to their incapacity, being idle and drunken ;—he resolves, in order to make up for this deficiency, upon taking more apprentices in addition to the undue number he already possesses—thus increasing the evil which the strike was intended to diminish. That this is a result characteristic of strikes, I have already proved in the case of the town above alluded to ; and if it were possible to ascertain the precise number of apprentices taken into the business by the Edinburgh employers during the last disastrous strike in that city, I have not the slightest doubt it would add considerable weight to the argument. " United to support, but not combined to injure," was the motto of the Northern Union ; and it was fully carried out, both in spirit and in letter ; for in every one of its strikes, while it carried desolation and misery into the homes of the *fair* and honourable men whom it compelled to engage in them, it afforded the greatest possible support to *rats* by closing offices, and thus *securing* permanent situations to men whom employers, under other circumstances, would on no account have upon their premises, owing to their inability as workmen, or their known dissolute character.

In conclusion I have to remark, that the importance of the subject must plead my excuse for these lengthy remarks, which certainly have extended over more paper than I at first intended. The objections I have urged against the too frequent occurrence of strikes, I trust will not be looked upon as the "shuffling and quixotic doctrines of a politico-economical enthusiast," nor yet "the puerile emanations of a distempered brain"—mere "paper theories, that melt into thin air the moment they are brought into contact with the sober realities of existence ;" but rather as the solid convictions of a heart that beats with a deep sympathy towards every kindred spirit that is anxious for the well-being of the profession at large. I am no opposer of legitimate combination, as I have stated at the commencement of this letter ; the "burden of my song" is still " unite, unite ! " for " divided " ye " fall "—and, in falling, will sink yet deeper into the pit, in which a fierce and remorseless spirit of competition has already engulphed you. In my next and last letter, I shall offer a few suggestions on the remedial part of the subject.

Wolverhampton.   J. Price.

* One of the men engaged in this strike had a family of six or seven depending upon him for a living—thus enhancing the value of the sacrifice ; and, to show the sympathy entertained towards this victim, after such noble conduct, I need only mention that, a few weeks after the occurrence, a tramp, a stranger to the town, was *put into a permanent situation ;* whilst the man who had thus suffered for the cause was allowed to walk the streets, getting a paltry job now and then. The great admirer of Diogenes, Rochefoucault, has a maxim which says—"There is something in the misfortunes of our dearest friends which does not displease us !" and certainly the conduct of the above parties would seem to prove that there was more of philosophic truth than cynicism in the remark !

We have been requested to acknowledge the receipt of the following subscriptions in aid of the Metropolitan Typographical, Widow, Orphan, or Nominee Fund :—On account of Dramatic Performance at the Royal Olympic Theatre (per Mr. Dorrington), 27*l.* 2*s.* 6*d.* ; V. G. Dowling, Esq., *Bell's Life* and *Observer* office, 5*l.* ; Proprietors of the *Daily News* (per Mr. Hartwell) 2*l.* 2*s.* ; Charles Cooke, Esq., *Morning Post,* annual, 10*s.* 6*d.* ; Mr. W. A. Law, 9, Catherine Street, 10*s.* 6*d.* ; Mrs. D. Arnot, 5*s.* ; and a donation of 5*s.* from each of the following gentlemen :—Mr. G. Sorbie, Mr. W. Tallent, and Mr. S. Bustin, *Daily News ;* Mr. D. Arnot and Mr. G. Roberts, *Morning Herald ;* Mr. J. Hawkes and Mr. C. L. Thetford, *Morning Post ;* Mr. W. A. Slyth and Mr. White, *Morning Chronicle ;* Mr. C. Scott, Mr. Lyons, Mr. Cooney, and Mr. Cockburn. The annual general meeting of the members will be held on the evening of the 11th instant. We feel happy in being enabled to state, that the Committee will present a favourable report as to the progress of the Society during the first year of its existence

THE LADY'S NEWSPAPER

With which is incorporated the Pictorial Times.

No. 219. SATURDAY, MARCH 8, 1851. [Price, 6d.

THE LADIES' CARPET,

WROUGHT BY ONE HUNDRED AND FIFTY LADIES, AND PRESENTED TO HER MAJESTY THE QUEEN

TO BE SHOWN AT THE GREAT EXHIBITION, HYDE PARK.

we should advise you to proceed to Hyde Park, where you will see (if you are not blind,)

THE CRYSTAL PALACE.

You may then light your pipe and stand with your back to the door, and as soon as it opens you are sure to go in. The first things to attract observation will be the following models:

A MODEL OF A STEAM-ENGINE AND TENDER,

A MODEL OF AN IRON STEAM BOAT,

drawn by those Industrious little animals, the Fleas. Passing along you will see the following articles:

Roasting Jack.   Kitchen Range.   Lock and Key.   Spring Bell.

Parlour Stove.   Horse Shoe.   Smoke Jack.

Cowls for Smoky Chimneys.

1.   2.   3.

1. Alarm Bell with Clock.
2. Iron Railing.
3. Gas Stove.

Passing from this part of the building you arrive at the place set apart for woollen goods.

THE RAW MATERIAL. | MADE UP.

No. 58.

UNDER THE PATRONAGE OF THE QUEEN.

DIEU ET MON DROIT

LE FOLLET,

JOURNAL DU GRAND MONDE,

Fashion, Polite Literature, Beaux Arts

&c., &c.

JULY, 1851.

PRICE ONE SHILLING AND SIXPENCE.

Paris:
69, BOULEVARD ST. MARTIN.

London
8, ARGYLL PLACE, REGENT STREET.

SIMPKIN, MARSHALL, & Co., Stationers' Court; SHERWOOD, GILBERT, & PIPER, Paternoster Row; and
may be had of all Booksellers in Town and Country.

39, CASTLE-STREET, HOLBORN.

THE
GENTLEMAN'S
MAGAZINE OF FASHION,

Published in Paris and London Monthly;

BY MONSIEUR DEVERE.

| NO. 39. | MARCH 1, 1851. | VOL. 4 |

Description of the Plates of Costumes.

PLATE THE FIRST.

Livery Costume. — Livery morning coat, buttoning to the throat in the tunic style; the skirt is full and short: the ends of the collar are each ornamented by two loops of silver lace in the form of a long buttonhole; the sleeves have broad cuffs and three buttons, one on the cuff the others on the sleeve. Breeches of white cord, they are of the form we have given in former numbers.

Lady's Riding Costume —Double-breasted habit of dark myrtle green ; the body is of the usual form with a lapel added : the sleeves are wide according to the present style, and have a broad cuff turned back. Waistcoat of white cashmere, buttoning to the throat, with a small collar turned down, and above which is worn a double frill of cambric.

Morning Costume.—Single-breasted frock coat, the pattern is given in our fifth plate, figs. 1, 2, 3 and 4. The sleeves have rather wide cuffs with two buttons, one on the cuff and the other on the sleeve. Waistcoat of the shawl form buttoning high.

PLATE THE SECOND.

Promenade Costume. — This is the back view of fig. 2, on the third plate ; the back is without seam in the middle ; we will here make a few remarks on the difficulties that occur to prevent the general adaptation of this style of back ; it is necessary that the bladebones should be of equal size and regular form ; the generality of men have one blade-bone larger than the other, and this requires of necessity, that the back should be cut in two pieces : we have given in former numbers several *paletots* with this style of back.

Travelling Costume.—Cloak of the color called *savoyard* brown ; the collar and facings of velvet : the form is the three-quarter circle, with extra width left on the front for buttoning over ; we have before given models of this style of cloak, with the exception of the extra width left on in front : all the edges are finished by a broad figured galloon.

Young Gentleman's Travelling Costume.— Caban of bright blue cloth : this is the style of caban occasionally worn by his Royal Highness the Prince of Wales when travelling ; there is no difference in the cut of this caban from the one given in the 4th plate of October, 1849.

PLATE THE THIRD.

Promenade Costume. — Single-breasted *paletot surtout*, the collar is of velvet ; it has a pocket in the left breast ; the front edge is finished by a broad galloon laid on flat ; the edge of the back skirt is also finished by this galloon which terminates at the notch : the cuff is not cut separate from the sleeve, but the sleeve is sprung out at the bottom to form the part that turns back ; it is lined with velvet.

Promenade Costume.—This is the front view of the 1st fig. on the 2nd plate : this *paletot* has the turnovers not cut separate, they are of a moderate width ; the collar is of velvet ; the sleeves are large, and the cuffs are drafted in the same manner as the first figure ; the top of the pockets, the flaps and the edges of this coat are finished by a broad galloon.

Evening Costume.—This coat is the same style as the dress coat we have given in our 4th plate. The waistcoat is of the narrow shawl form. The trowsers are tight in their whole length, and have very little spring at the bottom.

Written Music for the **Violin, Flute, Accordian, Cornopeon**
Instruction Books for all kinds of Instruments.

ALL SERENE!

Tune—Steam Arm   Written & sung by H. Wood

One Morning, a freak popped into my head,
  As I lay by the side of my wife in bed:
All was still throughout the house ;
  I crept from the sheets as still as a mouse.
      Ri to ro lo, ri to ri rido.

To clean myself I did repair,
  I left my wife a snoring there,
Collar and dickey nice and clean,
  Shiney boots and all serene.

On viewing the Exhibition bent,
  To view the things was my intent,
And there I saw our gracious Queen,
  What Harry my boy, you all serene.

She hoped that I was quite sublime,
  She'd stand a pot, but she'd not got time,
She hoped I would not think her mean,
  O no, says I, it's all serene.

At last I thought I'd leave the mob,
  I'd walked about enough for my bob,
I had drops of beer, and gin between,
  I found I was getting quite serene.

Some lads began to make their fun,
  Advised me much to take a run,
And asked if ma knew where I'd been,
  Ax my doudney 'tis all serene.

A maiden who was in the rear,
  Cried out, are you good natured dear,
She wore a gown of Bombazine,
  A jolly great bustle, and all serene.

She felt inclined for a bit of chat,
  We went to her aunts, and down we sat:
And then I found she was a Fleet-street queen,
  And, consequently, not serene.

I thought my wife my head would combe,
  When that I should venture home.
She said, you wretch where have you been,
  I said nothing. but all serene.

At last I felt quite glad to roll,
  To the bed from whence I stole.
I told my wife where I had been,
  I made it right, and all serene.
      Ri to ro lo, ri to ri rido.

Printed by T. King, Birmigham, and sold by Mr. Green, at his Music Stall, near the Turnpike, City-road, and at 27, Featherstone-street, City-road, where an extensive collection of old and new songs, harp and violin strings, fancy stationery, &c., may be had.

Tamborines, bows, screws, bridges, rosin, music paper

I'M GOING TO SEE
THE EXHIBITION
FOR A SHILLING.

LET all the world say what they will,
  I do not care a fig.
The Exhibition I will see,
  If I don't dash my wig ;
If I sell the pig and donkey,
  The frying pan and bed,
I will see the Exhibition
  While it is a bob a head.
     Never mind the rent or taxes,
      Dear Polly come with me,
     To the great Exhibition all
      The wonders for to see.

There's the dustman and chummy,
  Costermonger and the snob,
And every one in England
  That can only raise a bob :
From Manchester and Liverpool,
  Eleven millions strong,
With clever girls from
  Nine feet three inches long.
     Pull up your stockings Charlotte,
      And toddle off with me,
     Behind, nor yet before love,
      You never such did see.

There's up and downs, and ins and outs,
  Trafalgar and the Nile,
Down stairs and up, and round about,
  Is twenty-seven miles ;
There's coachman John, and footman Bill,
  And cookey on will trip,
While Bet, the housemaid, cuts along with
  Cabbage-nose, the snip.
     Clap on your bustle cookey,
      And haste along with me,
     To the great Exhibition love,
      A dripping pan to see.

There you may see king Alfred,
  And Billy Rufus bold,
Prince Albert all in silver,
  And Victoria made of gold ;
Queen Anne made out of bees' wax,
  On a wondrous pillar perched,
With her nose stuck in a gin shop,
  And her rump against the church.
     Come to the Exhibition
      Sweet Catherine with me,
     And for a bob a piece my love,
      Such funny things we'll see.

There's old king Hal, and old king George,
  Faith, Charity, and Hope,
There's old queen Bess on horseback,
  Going to fight the Pope ;
There's old king Ned in armour,
  King Stephen, and king jack,

jane Shore, and old king Richard,
  With a bible on his back.
     Put on your linen trousers, Sall,
      And come along with me,
     It is only love a shilling, all
      The wonders for to see.

Then syllabubs and sandwiches,
  Bath buns and nice cheese cakes,
Sew up your trouser's pocket, Tom,
  Some people make mistakes !
Nanny, hold your bustle up,
  And do not let it drop,
It is only twopence halfpenny for a
  Bottle of ginger pop.
     Come to the Exhibition,
      Dear Mary Anne, with me,
     And I will show you such a
      Nobby stunning rhubarb tree.

To tell of all the wonders
  That come from far away,
No one in England can repeat
  In a twelvemonth and a day ;
I saw a shining diamond,
  Worth seventy million pounds,
And a pair of spider's breeches
  All flounced unto the ground.
     Tie up your garters, Caroline,
      The Exhibition for to see,
     I have pawned my coat and trousers, love
      To pay for you and me.

Now is the time or never for
  To banish care and pain,
I'll bet a farthing cake you'll
  Never the chance again ;
The prize is but a shilling,
  To raise it spout your shoes,
Here's farmer Chubb and Dolly,
  Cock a doodle doo.
     Isabella, love, get ready,
      Along with me to trip,
     And you shall see the foreigners
      With their funny hairy lips.

And when that you have been to see
  The Exhibition grand,
Every class and all degrees
  From every distant land :
Your eyes will be so dazzled,
  That will affect your sconce,
You will ne'er be able for to sleep
  A wink for seven months.
     Hold up your bustle, fanny,
      And push along with me,
     And tell the folks when you get home,
      What wonders you did see.

Disley, Printer, Arthur-street, Oxford-street.

21

THE GREAT
NATIONAL EXHIBITION
OF 1851.

Printed by E. Hodges, (from Pitt's), wholesale Toy and Marble warehouse, 31, Dudley Street, Seven Dials.

WHAT wonderful times are coming, now
    mark,   [park
What wonderful scenes will be seen in Hyde
In the sweet month of May, & it will not be long
In the year eighteen hundred and fifty one;
All America, Asia, and Africa too,
The Russians, the Prussians, the Turks, & the Jews
The Soldier, the Sailor, the Peasant, & Nob,
The Tinker, the Tailor, the blacksmith & snob.

Look out for the wonders, it will n t be long,
In May, eighteen hundred and fifty-one,
By steam, land, and water, all nations will start,
To the Grand Exhibition, 'twill be in Hyde-park
There'll be new fashioned pokers, grid irons, and
    tongs.
Black puddings, and sausages seven feet long,
Hairy things for the ladies to hang down their
    backs
And bustles as long as a coalheaver's sack,
With wonderful presents for England's Queen,
And things for to get little children by steam,
With handsome machines for to cut ladies' corns
And new-fashioned bullocks without any horns,
There'll be the king and queen of Hong Kong,
With a wooden machine to grind old women
    young,   (of lead,
From the Africans' coast there'll be crowns made
And goats from the mountains with seventeen
    heads.   (shawls,
There'll be whiskers, and petticoats, garters, and
with muskets, and bayonets, and big canon balls
There'll be long sticks of cinnamon all in a row,
That will reach from Hyde-park into Stratford
    Le Bow,

There'll be ganders and geese, & pheasants a lot,
There'll be swung on a mop stick a tin iron pot,
From turkey nine ship loads of ribbons and veils
And a laughing Hyena that has seven tails.
All the trades in the world will be there in a
    mob.   [hods,
And the bricklayer's labourers too with their

This great Exhibition will dazzle your eyes
There's to be eighteen thousand come down]|
    from the skies.
There'll be lobsters, and pigeons, ard buffalo
    eggs,   (legs,
And from famed California some old wooden,
There'll be new fashioned spiders and new
    fashioned bees,
And new fashioned games under the trees,
The great big sea serpent is going to be there,
with old Brown and his salt box from Bartho-
    lomew Fair.
And to keep them alive there'll be Jinny Lind
And twenty-fine mermaids to merrily sing
There'll be new fashioned tables and gilt iron
    spoons,   [brooms,
There'll be new fashioned cradles and cast iron
There'll be great apple dumplins as big as a barn
With large sticks of rheubarb as long as my arm
Fifty thousand black damsels to London will roll
With sweet little banjo's as soft as a mole,
Such tunes on the grass they will merrily play,
At the great Exhibition that takes place in next
    May.

Tens of thousands of foreigners will all be met,
And in every corner lodgings to let,   (home,
The Lord, Duke, and Squire will toddle from
With the greasy old farmer and his loving Joan,
Such wonders since Adam was never seen,
There'll be Nosey and Johnny, King Al. and
    the Queen,
There'll be ladies in splendour so handsome and
    fine,   (behind.
And some with their shirts hanging right out
There'll be some wearing lockets to look at the
    fun,   (they come,
There'll be some picking pockets, and some as
Will take them, but soon they'll have to grin,
With a crack on the nose with a large rolling pin
It is out of my power the sights to explain,
We never before, and may never again,
Such wonders behold in the sweet month of May
As the National Great Exhibition, huzza !

The time is approaching, the season draws nigh
When every part of the world will be here,
with 22 millions coming dwn from the sky
Just on purpose to see if they can gain a p

CRYSTAL  PALACE

Tune, He'met on his brow.

Britannia's sons an attentive ear
  One moment lend to me,
Wether tillers of our fruitful soil
  Or lords of high degree
Mechanic too and artizan,
  Old Englands pride and boast
Whose wondrous skill has spread
    around
  Far far from Britain's coast.

For the great world's Exhibtion,
  Let's shout with loud huzza,
All nations never can forget
  The glorious First of May.

From every quarter of the globe
  They come across the sea,
And to the Chrystal Palace
  The wenders for to see.
Raised by the handiwork of men
  Born on British ground
A challenge to the universe
  Its equel to be found.

Each friendly nation in the world
  Have their asistance lent
And to this Exhibtion
  Have their productions sent;
And with honest zeal and ardour
  With pleasure do repair
With hands outstreched and gait
    erect
  To the world's great National
    Fair.

The Sons of England and France
  And America likewise,
with other Nations to contend
  To bear away the prise

with pride depicted in their eyes
  View the offspring of their hand
Oh surely England's greatest
    wealth
  Is an honest working man.

It is a glorions sight to see
  so many thousand's meet
Not heeding creed or country
  Each other friendly greet
Like children of one mighty sire,
  May that sacred tie ne'er ceas
May the blood stained sword of
    war give way
To the olive branch of peace.

But hark the trumpet's flourish
  Victoria does approach,
That she may long be spared tou,
  Shall be our reigning toast.
I trust each heart it will respond
  To what I now propose,
Good will & plenty to her friends
  And confusion to her foes.

Great praise is due to Albert
  For the good that he as done,
May others follow in his steps
  The work he has begun:
Then let us all with one accord,
  His name give with three cheers,
Shout huzza for the Chrystal
    Palace,
  And the world's great National
    Fair.

E Hodges from Pitts' 31. Dudley
street, 7 Dials

23

The Downfall of the Exhibition

I Have been free from storms and wars, and
I have been a gaze for tens of thousands,
Kings Queens and Princes did come first, then
After tailors sweeps and dussmen,
Every grade class and condition,
Came to see the Exhibiton,
Russians Prussians from over the seas sir,
Bears and donkeys bugs and fleas sir.
    Chorus
List from the land's end to Dover
I'm going to pot in sweet October,
Oh pity my downfall and condition
They've done up the National Exhibition

To look at me there was thousands willing,
And pawned their togs to raise a shilling,
And many went home like old Dan Tucker
Hurried to bed too late for supper,
And the next morning with downward head cast
Could not so much as raise a breakfast,
To see me they jump'd dykes and ditches
And up the spout shoved gowns and breeches.

Ladies came polonies munching,
Peelers came with wooden truncheons,
There were soldiers, sailors what a fuss then
Hackney coachmen, cabmen and bussmen
Workhouse people charity children,
Coalheavers and wives were bewildering,
Some thousands came from pass the Nile then,
And from all the Lunatic asylums.
    Oh, dear oh, my days are over,
    I must came down in sweet October.

I have pleased every rank and station,
I have surprised all foreign nations,
I have been a gaze for every noodle,
And a sight for every Yankee Doodle :
Officers with cheeks like monkeys,
Chinamen with hears like donkey,
Bakers Quakers Grocers Porters,
Farmer Chubb his wife and daughters.

Masons wheelwrights lawyers procters,
Butchers hangmen snobs and doctors,

Coachmen footmen and cooks in millions,
Nurses fidlers and postilions :
And thousands say of all condition,
Oh ! l ork ! have you seen the Exhibition !
By judges it is tried and cast sirs,
And the dreadful sentence on it passed sirs.

In a little time it must come down sirs,
And every bit cleared off the ground sirs
The committee say tis really curst hard,
They talk of turning it into a dust yard,
Before the glass they begin to hammer
They ought to let people in for a tanner,
The Knightsbridge folks vow it would be right
And pull a face as long as a cheese knife.

The railways had a tidy job sirs
since I was shewn for a single bob sirs,
Many a blooming maid did tustle
And sold her petticoat smock and bustle,
To have a peep at the chrystal glasses
Under the trees fell lads and lasses,
Thousands went home in a queer condition
To be put to bed with an Exhibition.

They from every town and village did strut sir,
Johnny Groats and Ballinamuck sirs,
Millions were together mingling
Scotland Ireland Wales and England,
France and Italy and the Nile then
The King and Queen of the Connibal Island,
Don Miguel and Baron Salder
The Prince of Hesse and the Queen of Malder

There never was such sights and tricks
since Adam dealt in leather breeches,
The Exhibition was, now mark sirs—
Nine times as big as Noah's Ark sirs,
some in the park began to bawl sirs,
They will turn it into a cobler's stall sirs,
or move it from there to a right spot
And make it into a stunning tripe shop

Paul, Printer, 18, Great St. Andrew street, Bloomsb.

EXHIBITION FASHIONS

COME listen with attention
  All ranks and all conditions,
Since every thing in England
  Is called the Exhibition :
There's Exhibition frying pans,
  And Exhibition hods,
There's Exhibition carpenters,
  And Exhibition snobs.

So everything we do behold
  In every condition,
From the palace to the cottage now
  Is called the Exhibition.

There's Exhibition bedsteads,
  And Exhibition pails,
There's Exhibition night caps,
  And Exhibition veils ;
There's Exhibition bustles,
  And there's Exhibition shoes,
And in many parts of London
  Exhibition doodle doos.

There's Exhibition broomsticks,
  And Exhibition knives,
The e's Exhibition rolling pins
  And Exhibition wives ;
There's Exhibition donkeys,
  And Exhibition flutes,
There's Exhibition sausages,
  And Exhibition boots.

There's Exhibition tables,
  And Exhibition chairs,
There's Exhibition cradles,
  And Exhibition fairs ;
There's Exhibition coffee,
  And there's Exhibition soap,
There's Exhibition parsons,
  And there's Exhibition popes.

There's Exhibition docters,
  And there's Exhibition hats,
There's Exhibition rabbits,
  And there's Exhibition cats ;
There's Exhibition saucepans,
  And Exhibition cheese,

And Exhibition washing tubs,
  And Exhibition fleas.

There's Exhibition garters,
  And Exhibition skirts,
There's Exhibition petticoats,
  And Exhibition shirts,
There's Exhibition barrows,
  And there's Exhibition eggs,
There's Exhibition soda,
  And there's Exhibition legs.

There's Exhibition watches,
  And there's Exhibition clocks,
There's Exhibition bonnets,
  And there's Exhibition smocks,
There's Exhibition gin shops,
  And Exhibition drums,
There's Exhibition soldiers,
  And there's Exhibition guns.

There's Exhibition shovels,
  And there's Exhibition whips,
There's Exhibition coaches,
  And there's Exhibition ships,
There's Exhibition sailors,
  And there's Exhibition wigs,
There's Exhibition tailors,
  And there's Exhibition pigs.

There's Exhibition baskets,
  And Exhibition songs,
There's Exhibition pokers,
  And there's Exhibition tongs ,
There's Exhibition farmers,
  And there's Exhibition ploughs,
There's Exhibition waggons,
  And there's Exhibition cows.

There's Exhibition pinbefores,
  And Exhibition rings,
There's Exhibition needles,
  And there's Exhibition pins
There's Exhibition omnibusses ,
  And Exhibition pens,
There's Exhibition women,
  And theres Exhibition men.

Hodges Printer Dudley St. Dials

THE
EXHIBITION
WONDERS.

W. M'Call, Printer, Cartwright Place, Byrom Street, Liverpool.
Shops and Hawkers supplied on the most reasonable terms.—
Upwards of 5,000 different sorts always on hand.

Good people all both great and small, come listen for awhile,
I'll sing to you a verse or two, will cause you for to smile,
Such wonders there was never seen, since first the world began,
As the Exhibition wonders, in the year of fifty one.

There never was such wonders
In old England before.

Go where you will by day or night, in town or country,
Such Exhibition wonders, you are certain for to see,
There is Exhibition herrings, salmon, mackerel and sprats,
Fine Exhibition bonnets, and silk Exhibition hats.

Exhibition knives and forks, coals, kettles, tubs, and cans,
Exhibition gates and bridges, dishes, plates, and frying pans,
There is Exhibition haddock, with oysters, crabs, and muscles,
And for the pretty ladies, there is Exhibition bustles.

There is Exhibition gin & rum, combs, brushes, thread, & flocks'
Exhibition straw & feather beds, dickeys, handkerchiefs & stocks,
There is Exhibition coffins for the people when they die,
And Exhibition birds to sing Susannah don't you cry.

There is Exhibition cabbages, potatoes, greens and toys,
There is Exhibition sausages, black puddings and pork pies,
There is Exhibition malt and hops, with flour, wheat and corn,
And some Exhibition children, next year they will be born.

Exhibition pills and physic, carts, carriages and gigs,
Exhibition tea and coffee, and some Exhibition prigs,
There is Exhibition candles, soap, soda, starch and cheese,
Exhibition sheets and blankets too, for catching all the fleas.

There is Exhibition boots and shoes, shirts, breeches & top coats,
And Exhibition razors, if you wish to cut your throats,
There is Exhibition gowns and shawls, with petticoats & smocks,
Exhibition pigeons, geese and hens, and Exhibition cocks.

There is Exhibition horses, donkeys, billy-goats and cows,
Exhibition harrows, rakes and forks, and Exhibition ploughs,
Exhibition things to thrash the corn, and Exhibition spades,
And some Exhibition rhubarb, for to please the pretty maids.

There is Exhibition parsley, cauliflowers, mint and sage,
And there's Exhibition farmers, to grind down the servant's wage,
There's ploughboys to plough the land, and tars to plough the sea
And Exhibition milk maids for to roll upon the hay.

There's Exhibition cups and saucers, coffins, buttermilk & swipes
Exhibition 'bacco and cigars, and Exhibition pipes,
There is exhibition butter, sugar, bacon, ham, and bread,
And exhibition bugs to bite you, when your fast asleep in bed.

This glorious exhibition has gave everything a name,
From a needle to an anchor, you will find it just the same
The famous exhibition will for years be talked upon,
And the great and glorious wonders that was seen in fifty one.

ELLEN THE FAIR

Fair Ellen one morning from her cottage had stray'd
To the next market town tript this beautiful maid,
She look'd like a goddess, so charming and fair,
Come buy my sweet posies, cried Ellen the fair.

I have cowslips, I have jessamine, and air-bells so blue
Wild roses and eglantine, all glisten'd with dew,
The lilly, the queen of the valley so fair,
Come buy my sweet posies, cried Ellen the fair.

With rapture I gazed on this beautiful maid,
Whilst thousand sweet smiles on her countenance play'd
And while I stood gazing, my heart, I declare,
A captive was made by Ellen the fair.

And if I could gain this fair one for my wife,
How gladly I would change my condition in life,
I would forsake the folks and the town, and repair
To dwell in the cottage with Ellen the fair.

What need I care for the lords or the great,
My parents are dead, I've a noble estate,
No lady on earth, nor princess shall share
My hand or my fortune, but Ellen the fair.

A little while after this nobleman's son,
Did marry the maid his affections had won ;
While present in court, the merchants did stare,
And the ladies all envied sweet Ellen the fair.

400

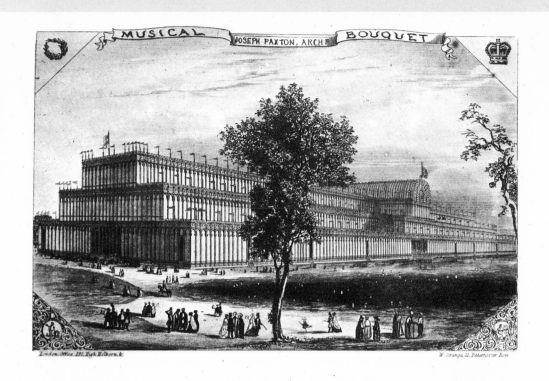

THE GREAT EXHIBITION WALTZ of 1851.

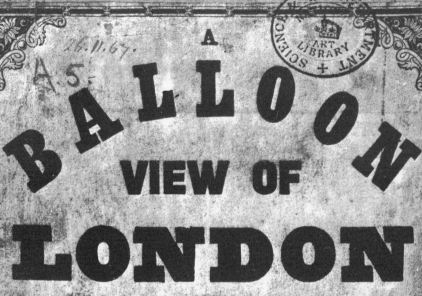

A
BALLOON
VIEW OF
LONDON

TAKEN

BY THE DAGUERREOTYPE PROCESS,

(SIZE OF ENGRAVING 43 BY 25 INCHES,)

EXHIBITING EIGHT SQUARE MILES,

SHEWING

ALL THE RAILWAY STATIONS

PUBLIC BUILDINGS,

PARKS, PALACES, SQUARES, STREETS, &c.,

With their Names clearly Written,

FORMING

A COMPLETE STREET GUIDE.

In Sheet, 1s. ; In Case for the Pocket, 1s. 6d.

London:
APPLEYARD & HETLING,
86, FARRINGDON STREET.

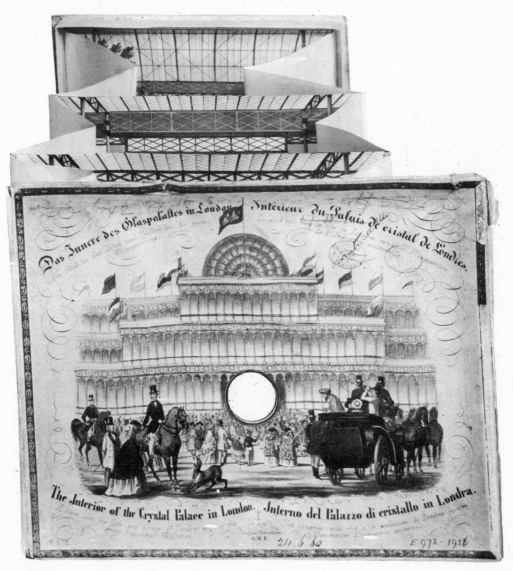

The Interior of the Crystal Palace in London.

30

The Transept and Nave—Great Exhibition

The Building for the Exhibition of 1851

REFERENCE.

AA   *The blank pieces of paper on the feeding table.*
B   *The feeder.*
C   *The exhausting bellows.*
D   *The folding box.*
E   *The creaser or plunger.*

FF   *The slits or openings through which the currents of air are forced, for giving the requisite inclination to the flaps of the partially-formed envelope.*
G   *The bellows by which the currents of air are produced.*

H   *The shoot.*
I   *The gum dabber.*
K   *The gum cistern.*
L   *The die for embossing.*

THIS Machine, exhibited by MESSRS. WATERLOW AND SONS, of London Wall, London, introduces an ingenious application of atmospheric pressure, which is employed for the purposes of transporting the piece of paper to form the envelope, from the table on which it is placed to the top of the folding apparatus, and giving the necessary inclination to the flaps of the partially-formed envelope previous to its being completed by the action of the creaser.

The Machine works in the following manner:—Three or four hundred pieces of paper, to form the envelopes, are placed on the feeding table AA, and the Machine is then started. The top sheet is raised singly from the pile on the table, by means of a flat hollow feeder B, the under side of which is perforated, and a vacuum being formed by exhausting the air by the bellows, C, connected with it by an elastic tube, the sheet is sucked up against the under surface, and the feeder at that instant rushing forward, conveys it to the folding-box, D, when the vacuum is destroyed, and the sheet drops into its place. The folding box is an open frame, the size of the required envelope, over which is fixed the creaser or plunger, E, which fits the inside of the frame accurately. The sheet having been deposited on the folding box, as before mentioned, the creaser descends within the box, and the flaps of the envelope are thus bent to a right angle. The bottom of the box is perforated, to prevent any atmospheric resistance on the entrance of the paper, and the creaser, rising, leaves the sheet within the box, with its four flaps upright. It is now obvious that some agency is required to give the upright flaps of the envelope such a deviation from the perpendicular as will fit them for receiving the second stroke of the creaser, which completes the envelope. For this purpose, four slits, FF, are made in the sides of the folding box, through which strong currents of air are forced, from the bellows, G, beneath, obliquely, on the flaps of the envelope (previously upright), and while they are in a consequent inclined position, the creaser again descends, and completes the envelope, which passes away, down the shoot, H, to the person waiting to receive it. It will be observed that, in the process just described, reference only is made to the *folding* of the envelope, but it is also *gummed* and *embossed* simultaneously with the other part of the process. At the instant immediately preceding the *first* descent of the creaser, the envelope, (then, of course, in a flat state,) is pressed by the dabber, I, on to two apertures, through which the gum oozes from the cistern, K, and, at the same moment, the die, L, is impressed on the opposite flap of the envelope.

It will be readily perceived that the *cams* fixed on the shaft above direct the successions of the above movements, which, of course, are very rapid; the Machine being able to produce from 30 to 35 complete envelopes per minute.

FOLDING MACHINE.

Folding and Gumming 60 Envelopes per Minute, or 3600 per Hour,
at the GREAT EXHIBITION OF 1851.

Made and Exhibited by

THOMAS DE LA RUE & COMPANY.

Show Rooms, Bunhill Row, Finsbury.

WATERLOW'S
Patent Improved Autographic Press.

By means of which a Clerk or Porter may Print Circular Letters, &c, &c, with ease and despatch, and secures that privacy so often requisite in Bank Correspondence.

Full particulars forwarded free, upon application to Waterlow & Sons, London.

Printed by the Autographic Press.

37

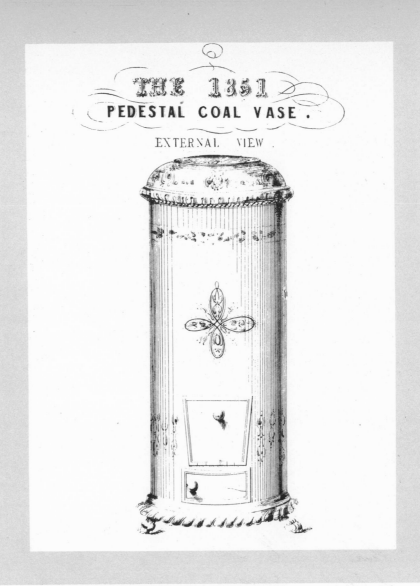

THE 1851
PEDESTAL COAL VASE.

EXTERNAL VIEW.

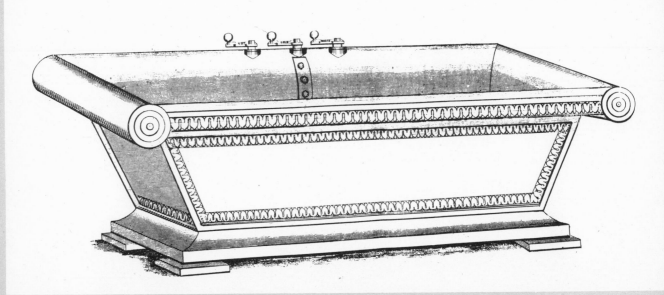

18. A Grecian bath with Cocks no Shower

38

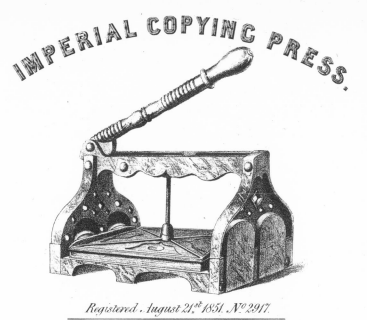

IMPERIAL COPYING PRESS.

Registered. August 21.st 1851. N.o 2917.

Manufactured by W. Pearce, 38, Loyd Street, Green Heys, Manchester.

Stephens' Fountain Ink-Holder.

FIGURE 1.

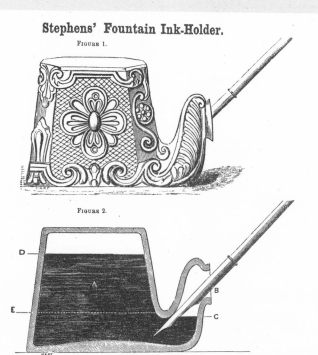

FIGURE 2.

Figure 1 is an external view of STEPHENS' FOUNTAIN INK HOLDER.

Figure 2 is a section, shewing its interior construction and arrangement, and illustrative of its principles of action. (A) is the body of the Ink-holder. (B) the mouth. (C) the surface of the ink in the mouth, shewing the position of the pen in dipping and the extent of its immersion. (D) the maximum level of the ink. (E) the minimum level, or point at which the fountain principle ceases to act.

In the use of this Ink-holder, it may be remarked, that if a *small* quantity of ink is contained in the holder, say down to line (E,) the quantity of air contained will be considerable—a fire in the room, or the influence of the sun upon the Ink-holder, acting upon and expanding this larger body of confined air, causes it to press upon the surface of the ink, and gives it a tendency to overflow the mouth; but the height and lateral extension of the mouth of this Ink-holder is calculated to compensate for the expansion within, so that this effect never takes place in this improved Ink-holder.

White Flint Glass	. 2s. 0d. each	White Porcelain	. . 2s. 0d. each
Coloured ditto	. 2s. 6d. „	Decorated ditto	. . 2s. 9d. „

54, Lower Stamford Street, Blackfriars' Road, London.

FIRE-RESISTING SAFE.

HOLDFAST & FIRE-RESISTING.

List No. 2.

No. 1.—£8 5s.

24in. high
18 wide
18 deep

No. 2.—£10.

26 high
20 wide
20 deep

No. 3.—£12.

28 high
22 wide
22 deep

No. 4.—£16.

30 high
24 wide
24 deep

No. 4½.—£18.

32 high
26 wide
26 deep

No. 5—£21 15s

30 high
30 wide
24 deep

No. 6.—£26.

33 high
33 wide
27 deep

No. 7.—£30.

36 high
36 wide
30 deep

List No. 3.

No. 1.
£15 7s. 6d.
24 in. high
18 wide
18 deep

No. 2.—£18.

26 high
20 wide
20 deep

No. 3.—£21.

28 high
22 wide
22 deep

No. 4.—£24.

30 high
24 wide
24 deep

No. 4½.—£27.

32 high
26 wide
26 deep

No. 5.

£32 12s. 6d.
30 high
30 wide
24 deep

No. 6.—£39
33 high
33 wide
27 deep

No. 7.—£45.
36 high, 36 wide
30 deep

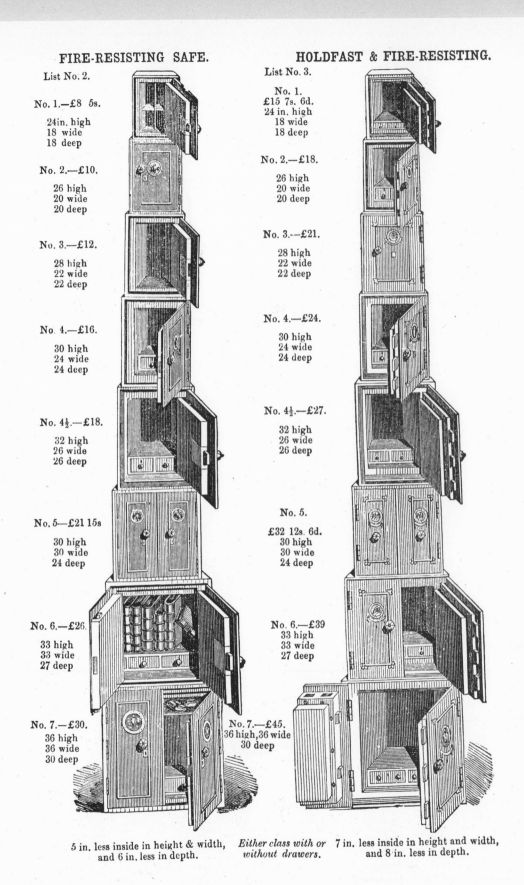

5 in. less inside in height & width,
and 6 in. less in depth.

Either class with or without drawers.

7 in. less inside in height and width,
and 8 in. less in depth.

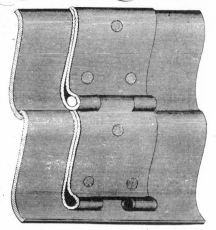

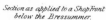
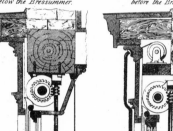
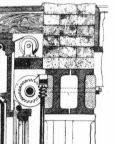

41

The  Times.

Nº. 20,886.   LONDON, THURSDAY, AUGUST 21, 1851.   PRICE, WITH A SUPPLEMENT, 5d.

NORWICH UNION FIRE INSURANCE SOCIETY.

ESTABLISHED   M.DCC.XCVII.

Capital . . £550,000.

GOVERNMENT DUTY (1849) £72,241. 15s.   FARMING STOCK INSURED £9,722,490.

By the constitution of this Society, three-fifths of the surplus Premiums are allotted to the Assured, who have thus received, from time to time, returns amounting in the aggregate to nearly £350,000; while at the same time they are free from all responsibility on account of its engagements.

The last return was declared at Michaelmas 1846.

The Premiums charged by this Office are upon the most moderate scale, and in no case higher than those required by other Offices making no return to their Insurers.

The return is made upon all Policies, whether annual or for shorter periods.

NORWICH UNION LIFE INSURANCE SOCIETY.

(ESTABLISHED 1808.)

This Society has been established upwards of forty years upon the principles of Mutual Assurance, during which period it has paid to claimants, on terminated Policies, upwards of £3,000,000, in addition to which nearly One Million sterling has been assigned by way of Bonuses. The invested capital of this Society amounted upon the 30th of June last to £2,120,000. 12s. 8d. and consisted of the general capital account £1,945,675, and the reserved fund of £174,324. 13s. 6d.

The annual income, according to the balance-sheet then audited, amounting to £957,482. 2s. 11d. of which £162,671. 4s. 4d. was received on account of Annual Premiums.

There is no proprietary to divide with the assured the profits of this Institution, which are therefore periodically assigned in addition made to the sums assured.

The attention of the Public is called to the magnitude of the reserved Bond, in greater than the subscribed capital of most Insurance Offices, and which, instead of proving source of temptation, as the subscribed capital of a proprietary body must necessarily be, must in this Society become the parent of future bonuses, from the 30th June 1849, to the same date 1850, 21 & 8 Policies were out with an increase of 5 upon the year, a number strongly demonstrating the public confidence in this Society.

One-half of the first five Annual Premiums may remain upon Policies granted for the whole duration of life.

For Prospectuses of both Societies apply to the Offices, Birchin-lane, London; and Surrey-street, Norwich.

43

DEAN AND SON'S
ORIGINAL AND SUPERIOR
COLOURED SIX-PENNY BOOKS.

GRANDMAMMA EASY's PICTORIAL BOOKS.

Merry Multiplication
Tom Thumb and his Mother
Stories of the Alphabet
Old Daddy Longlegs
Little Jack Horner
Cock Robin Alive & well again
Poor Molly Goosey
Alderman's Feast: an Alphabet
Buildings of London
Wonders of a Toy Shop
Little Matty Macaroni
Queen of Hearts & the Tarts
Stories of the Elephant
Stories of the Camel

GRANDPAPA EASY'S PICTORIAL BOOKS.

General Tom Thumb
Dame Bantry and her Cat
New Mother Goose
Two Sisters
Little Pig's Ramble
Jacko's Merry Pence Table
Lady Golightly
Lion and the Unicorn
History of Tom Pepper
Amusing Addition
Poetry about Trees, Fruits, &c.
New Puss in Boots
Poetical Spelling Book
Countries of Europe

COUSIN HONEYCOMB's NEW SERIES.

Amusing Multiplication
Amusing Division
Amusing Subtraction
Amusing Pence Table
Alphabet of Trades & Industry
Popular Nursery Rhymes
Popular Riddles and Puzzles
Tales of the Months & Seasons
Royal A B C, & Spelling-Book
Aunt's Ball : a New Alphabet
Railway Alphabet
The Mouse and her Sons
Prince and his Three Gifts
Story of Little Joey

UNCLE BUNCLE'S PICTORIAL BOOKS.

Alphabet of Objects
Second Alphabet of Objects
Peter's Visit to the Farm
Little Cottage Children
Comical Boys
about Master Nobody
about Birds
Johnny Green
Harry, the Sailor Boy
B C
about Animals
Little Robin, and his
Jenny Wren
Mayor's Show

SCRIPTURAL SERIES, NEW SUNDAY BOOKS.

Scripture Historical Alphabet
Two Brothers : Cain and Abel
History of Isaac and Rebekah
History of Esau and Jacob
Joseph and his Brethren
History of Moses
History of Samuel
History of Ruth and Naomi
History of David
Elisha : and the Widow's
    Cruise of Oil
Disobedient Prophet
Daniel, or Captives of Judah
History of Our Saviour

AUNT BUSY BEE'S NEW SERIES.

Comic Alphabet, with Verses
Alphabet of Flowers
Little Frog and Pretty Mouse
Fine Palace the Prince built
Little John and Silver Shilling
Two Brothers and the Echo
Stories: Horses, Dogs, Ships
New London Cries
Alphabet of Nouns and Objects
Whittington and his Cat
Gamut & Time Table in Verse
Mouse in a Christmas Cake
Peep at the Zoological Gardens
Peter Paganini

THE SCRIPTURAL SERIES OF NEW SUNDAY BOOKS, are also printed in 8mo. Super Royal, price Six-pence each History,—embellished with similar accurate Engravings ;—or the whole Series, Bound in Two Elegant Volumes, entitled THE PICTURE NURSERY SUNDAY BOOK, for Young Children, 7s.

ELEGANT TOILET REQUISITES.

EACH OF INFALLIBLE ATTRIBUTES.

Under the Patronage of the several Sovereigns & Courts of Europe, & universally preferred & esteemed.

ROWLAND'S MACASSAR OIL.

THE unprecedented success of Rowland's Macassar Oil, either in preserving the hair in its original strength and beauty or restoring it when lost, is universally known and appreciated: and recorded by testimonials most numerous in themselves, & certified by the highest authorities. It has obtained the exclusive patronage of Royalty, not only as regards our own Court, but those of the whole of Europe. From its exquisite purity and delicacy, it is admirably adapted for the hair of children, even of the most tender age, and is constantly employed for this purpose in the Nursery of Royalty, and by the families of the nobility and aristocracy. It is alike suited for either sex; and whether employed to embellish the tresses of female beauty, or to add to the attractions of manly grace and aspect, will be found an indispensible auxiliary to the toilet both of ladies and gentlemen.

Price 3s. 6d., 7s., Family Bottles, (equal to 4 small) 10s. 6d., and, double that size, 21s. per Bottle.

THE SYRENS.

"With bright and flowing Hair!"

      ANON.

"—— the songs of Syrens sweet,"

"Summer drouth, and singed air,
Never scorch your Tresses fair!"

      MILTON.

ROWLAND'S KALYDOR,

For the Skin and Complexion. This preparation, eminently balsamic, restorative, and invigorating, is equally distinguished for safety in application, as for unfailing efficacy in eradicating all redness, tan, pimples, spots, freckles, discolorations, and other cutaneous visitations. The radiant bloom it imparts to the cheek, and the softness and delicacy which it induces on the hands and arms, render it indispensable to every toilette.

To ladies during the period of nursing, and as a wash for infants it cannot be too strongly recommended.

Gentlemen, after shaving, will find it allay all irritation and tenderness of the skin, and render it soft, smooth, and pleasant. As a renovating and refreshing Wash during the heat and dust of Summer, or frost and bleak winds of Winter; and, in cases of Sunburn Stings of Insects Chilblains, Chapped Skin, or Incidental Inflammation, its virtues have long and extensively been acknowledged.

Price 4s. 6d. and 8s. 6d. per Bottle.

THE GRACES.

"The Graces ——
Hither all their bounties bring."

"Too divine to be mistook."

"To whom our vows and wishes bend:
Here our solemn search have end.
Fame, that their high worth to raise,
Seemed erst so lavish and profuse,
We may justly now accuse
Of detraction from their praise!"

      MILTON.

ROWLAND'S ODONTO.

OR PEARL DENTIFRICE, a White Powder, compounded of the choicest and most recherche Ingredients of the Oriental Herbal, of inestimable value in preserving and beautifying the Teeth, strengthening the Gums, and in rendering the breath sweet and pure. It extirpates all tartarous adhesions to the Teeth, and insures a pearl-like whiteness to the enamelled surface. Its Anti-Septic and Anti-Scorbutic properties exercise a highly beneficial and salutary influence; they arrest the further progress of decay of the Teeth, induce a healthy action of the Gums, and cause them to assume the brightness and colour indicative of perfect soundness; while by confirming their adhesion to the Teeth, they give unlimited enjoyment and fresh zest to appetite, by perpetuating effective and complete mastication. It speedily removes those ravages which children sustain in the Teeth owing to the improper use of sweet and acid compounds.

Price 2s. 9d. per box.

EUPHROSYNE.

"—— bring with thee
Health and youthful jollity,
Quips and cranks, and wanton wiles,
Nods and becks, and wreathed smiles!"

"—— Saw you her TEETH?
When she is near the pearl forgets to shine!"

      THE MAY QUEEN.

ROWLAND'S HAIR WASH.

This is a preparation from the choicest Oriental Herbs, of peculiarly mild and detersive properties. It pleasingly and effectually cleanses the Hair and Skin of the Head from Scurf and every species of impurity, and imparts a delicate fragrance. It is particularly recommended to be used after Bathing, as it will prevent the probability of catching cold in the head, and will render the hair dry in a few minutes. It entirely supersedes the necessity for using the fine comb, so injurious to the tender skin of the head; and from its beneficial effects on the health, together with the grateful and refreshing sensation it imparts, and, being perfectly innocent in its nature, will prove an invaluable appendage to the toilet, and the purposes of the Nursery.

Price 3s. 6d. per Bottle.

SABRINA.

"Sabrina, fair,
Listen where thou art sitting,
Under the glassy, cool, translucent wave,
In twisted braids of lilies knitting
The loose train of thy amber-dropping hair!"

"—— She sits on diamond rocks,
Sleeking her soft, alluring locks."

      MILTON.

BEWARE OF SPURIOUS IMITATIONS.

The ONLY GENUINE of each bears the Name of "ROWLANDS," preceding that of the Article on the Wrapper or Label with the signature at the foot, in Red Ink, thus—

A. ROWLAND AND SONS,

Sold by them at 20, Hatton Garden, London: and by every respectable Chemist and Perfumer throughout the Kingdom.

THE MOST SUCCESSFUL and POPULAR THEATRE IN LONDON!

ANOTHER WEEK OF GLORIOUS TRIUMPH!

'MAZEPPA,'

THE MOST ATTRACTIVE SPECTACLE EVER PRODUCED.

CROWDED TO THE CEILING NIGHTLY!

On MONDAY, AUGUST 11th, 1851, (and DURING THE WEEK)

The Curtain will rise at 7 o'clock, to LORD BYRON's highly Successful and Popular Spectacle (with New Scenery, Costumes, Dresses, & Decorations,) of

MAZEPPA!
AND THE

WILD HORSE!

Which has been presented with the greatest possible care, with ALL its Original, Extraordinary and Brilliant Effects.

The Scenery by Mr. DALBY.   Machinery by Mr. RICHARD SMITH.   Costumes by Mr. BOVEY and Mrs MEEK.   Decorations and Properties by Mr. MORRIS.   Dances by Mr. W. H. HARVEY.   The Original Music led by Mr. PHILLIPS.

The whole re-produced under the immediate Superintendance of Mr. T. THOMPSON.

POLES—The Castellan of Laurinski.......................................Mr. JOHNSON.
Premislaus....................................(Count Palatine)..........................Mr. A. STIRLING
Rudzeloff.............................(Chamberlain of the Household)...................Mr. S. SMITH
Drolinski.......................Mr. T. BARRY   Sentinel..........................Mr. JOHN
Olinska...............................(Daughter of the Castellan).................Miss FENTON
Agatha.............(her Nurse)...........Mrs. BEACHAM   Zemila..............Miss F. GARTHWAITE
Knights, Officers, Guards, Heralds, Domestics, Ladies, &c. &c.
TARTARS—Abder Khan....................(King of Tartary).......................Mr. CROWTHER
Mazeppa.............(his Son, under the name of Cassimer).......Mr. N. T. HICKS
Thamar.......(a conspiring Chieftain).....Mr. DANAVILLE   Zemba............Mr. CRADDOCK
Kadne and Kessar.............(Tartar Shepherds).................Mr. STICKNEY and Mr. W. H. HARVEY
Rider.................................Mr. REGAN
Oneiza.........Mrs. MORETON BROOKES   Shepherdess.........Mrs. W. H. HARVEY

46

In the course of this Splendid Spectacle, will be vividly pourtrayed, the powerful description in the Poem of "Mazeppa and the Wild Horse," commencing with the

SPLENDID CORTEGE—Nuptial Procession of the Palatine's Envoy, and Ceremony of affiancing a Polish Bride.

COURT YARD of the CASTLE of
LAURINSKI (Night).

GRAND ARENA of the CASTLE
Carousal and Chivalric Sports.

TOURNAMENT AND CONTEST OF MOUNTED KNIGHTs.
TERRACES AND GARDENS OF THE CASTLE.

"The Horse was brought,
In truth he was a noble Steed,
A Tartar of the Ukrain breed,
Who look'd as though the speed of thought

Were in his limbs—but he was wild,
Wild as the wild Deer, and untaught;
With spur and bridle, undefiled.
They bound me on that menial thong,

Upon his back, with many a thong;
Then loosed him with a sudden lash
Away, away! and on we dash,
Torrents less rapid, and less rash."

MAZEPPA AND THE WILD HORSE!
DELINEATED BY A MOVING
PANORAMA & LIVING HORSE!

Pourtraying the course of the Dneiper with Mountainous Country—Descent of the Eagle and all the Horrible Accompaniments of his Flight.
"It is no dream, the Wild Horse stems the Wilder stream."

Wild Cattle of the Desert—The Storm—Mazeppa on the EXHAUSTED AND WORN-OUT STEED, who sinks beneath his fatigue—**TARTAR TENT!** —Mazeppa rescued, preserved from the Plots of Assassins, and PROCLAIMED KING OF TARTARY. GRAND

PLAINS OR STEEPES OF TARTARY

Rural Sports and Songs of Tartar Shepherds—Dread Tradition of "the Volpes"—

ENCAMPMENT OF the TRIBES!
Review of TartarForces, Horse & Foot & departureforthe

INVASION OF POLAND!

Ramparts, Battlements, and Donjon keep in the Castle of Laurinski—Bridal Festival!

CHARACTERISTIC PAS DE DEUX, by Mr. & Mrs. W. H. HARVEY
DESTRUCTION OF THE CASTLE AND
TRIUMPH OF MAZEPPA.

AFTER WHICH, BATTY'S GRAND
SCENES: THE ARENA

Introducing the Largest Equestrian Company in Europe; represented by the Foreign and British Artistes, Male and Female.

Commencing with **Signor CHIARINI**, in his Incomparable Act of Riding, Driving, and Managing.

SIX HORSES!

After which, AMELIA BRIDGES will introduce Mr. BATTY's Highly-trained Spotted Barb,

'TAGLIONI!'
IN THE HIGH SCHOOL OF TRAINING.

LA PETITE JEANNETTE, the Youngest Equestrian of the Present Day, in a Pleasing

SCENE D'EQUITATION

To be followed by a Graceful Pageant, introducing Eight of the Principal Ladies and Gentlemen Equestrians, with their Steeds, entitled the

STAR & WALTZ
ENTREE!

To be succeeded by **Mr. C. ADAMS**, the Celebrated Equestrian, in his celebrated Shaksperian Characters of

SIR JOHN FALSTAFF, SHYLOCK,
AND
RICHARD III.

That Accomplished Artiste, Mdlle. GARDONI, in her much admired and celebrated Scene of the

LEAP OF STREAMERS

AMELIA BRIDGES will have the honour of appearing in her admired Act, of

JOAN OF ARC!

The Arena Amusements will terminate with Mr. JOHN BRIDGES, the

FIRST BRITISH HORSEMAN
OF THE DAY, as the Bounding Springer of the Alps

The Performances in the Arena will be enlivened by the Drolleries of the Unrivalled Jesters........Mr. T. BARRY, the Celebrated Hibernian Clown and Mr. WHEAL, the Gymnastic Buffoon.
Riding Masters..Signor CHIARINI and Mr. WIDDICOMB

The Entertainments concluding with EVERY EVENING, the Laughable Afterpiece of

JACK JUNK.

Captain Bertram............................Mr. JOHNSON,	Jack Junk...............................Mr. S. SMITH
Mr. Caplas................Mr. CROWTHER,	Harry.....................................Mr. A. STIRLING,
Mr. Bertram.........................	Mr. LLOYD,
Mrs. Moral....................Mrs. MORETON BROOKES,	Emma...............................Mrs. BEACMAN.

Stage Manager, - - - - - - Mr. T. THOMPSON,
Late of the THEATRE ROYAL, DRURY LANE.

47

MIDLAND RAILWAY.

TO LONDON & BACK
IN COVERED CARRIAGES,
For 5s. ! ! !

REDUCED FARES!!

REDUCED FARES!!

Excursion Passengers may book to LONDON TWICE EVERY DAY (until further notice,) by Trains advertised via the Midland route at the following REDUCED FARES:

	First Class.		Second Class.		Covered Third Class.	
	s.	d.	s.	d.	s.	d.
From York - - -	18	0	10	0	5	0
„ Bradford - -	18	0	10	0	5	0
„ Leeds - -	18	0	10	0	5	0
„ Normanton -	18	0	10	0	5	0
„ Wakefield Town	18	0	10	0	5	0

First & Second Class Passengers allowed 21 days in London, and Third Class 14 days.

The Tickets are available to return with by Special Trains leaving Euston Station every Monday and Saturday at 6.45 a.m., on Wednesdays at 11.0 a.m., AND EVERY DAY by Mail Train at 9.0 p.m.

By Order, JOSEPH SANDERS, General Manager.

Derby, July 29nd., 1851.

PRINTED BY W. BEMROSE & SON, DERBY.

49

TAKE CARE THAT YOU BUY
ALLEN'S ORIGINAL EDITION.
This caution is necessary to prevent imposition.

POOR RICHARD'S
PENNY
ALMANACK,
AND
FIRE-SIDE COMPANION,
FOR
1852.

CONTENTS:—

This Almanack may also be had INTERLEAVED, *price 2d.; or with a complete* DIARY *attached, sewed, 4d.; half-bound, 6d.*

LONDON:
PUBLISHED BY GEORGE VICKERS, STRAND;
AND SOLD BY ALL WHOLESALE STATIONERS AND BOOKSELLERS.

51

A GOOD CHARACTER IS A FORTUNE.

Side panel (vertical): RICHES TAKE TO THEMSELVES WINGS, AND FLY AWAY.

Side panel (vertical): TRUE ECONOMY IS SOMETHING BETTER THAN STINGINESS.

SEPTEMBER, 30 Days.
Last QR. 6d. 6·34 after | 1st QR. 20d. 1·17 after
N. Moon 13d. 10·38 after | F. Moon 28d. 6·24 morn

1	W	Giles. Part. sh. beg.	Hot	5 13
2	T	Chol. rag. in Eng. 1849	Hot	6 43
3	F	O. Cromwell d. 1658	Hot	5 17
4	S	Blake b. 1657	Win.	6 39
5	S	13 Sun. after Trinity	Fair	5 20
6	M	Hannah More d. 1833	Fair	6 34
7	T	Enurchus	Fair	5 23
8	W	Nativity of B. V. M.	Show	6 30
9	T	Jeru. tak. by Titus, 70	Fair	5 26
10	F	Tea first Imp. 1391	Fair	6 25
11	S	Lord Thurlow d. 1806	Show	5 29
12	S	14 Sun. after Trinity	Fair	6 20
13	M	Wolfe killed, 1759	Fair	5 33
14	T		Fair	6 16
15	W	Nap. en. Moscow, 1812	Cha.	5 36
16	T	New York taken, 1777	Cha.	6 11
17	F	C. G. Hope, cap. 1795	Fair	5 38
18	S	Geo. 1st landed, 1714	Fair	6 6
19	S	15 Sun. after Trinity	Show	5 42
20	M	Ld. Brougham b. 1779	Fair	6 2
21	T	St. Matthew	Fair	5 45
22	W	Gn. Pt. Office op. 1829	Cha.	5 57
23	T	Autumn Qr. begins	Cha.	5 49
24	F	Charles I. deth. 1640	Cha.	5 53
25	S	Mrs. Hemans b. 1794	Fair	5 52
26	S	16 Sun. after Trinity	Show	5 48
27	M	J. Brindley d. 1772	Sqal.	5 55
28	T	Wil. of Wykm. d. 1404	Fair	5 44
29	W	Michael. Mich. Day	Fair	5 58
30	T	G. Whitfield d. 1770	Fair	5 39

Battle of Trafalgar, 1805.

OCTOBER, 31 Days.
Last QR. 6d. 10·36 morn | 1st QR. 19d. 11·55 after
N. Moon 13d. 7·14 morn | F. Moon 27d. 11·54 after

1	F	Remigius. Phe. sh. b.	Fair	6 1
2	S	Lon. Univ. Col. op. 1828	Rain	5 34
3	S	17 Sun. after Trinity	Cold	6 5
4	M	Bishop Heber d. 1833	Cold	5 30
5	T	Kirke White d. 1806	Fair	6 8
6	W	Louis Philippe b. 1773	Fair	5 25
7	T		Frost	6 12
8	F	Erskine died, 1817	Fair	5 21
9	S	St. Denys	Fair	6 15
10	S	18 Sun. after Trinity	Rain	5 17
11	M	Old Michaelmas Day	Fog	6 18
12	T	Battle of Jena, 1806	Cold	5 12
13	W	Trans. of Edwd. Con.	Fair	6 22
14	T	W. Penn b. 1644	Fair	5 8
15	F	Koskiusco died 1817	Fair	6 25
16	S	Houses of Par. b. 1834	Fair	5 4
17	S	19 Sun. after Trinity	Rain	6 29
18	M	St. Luke	Rain	4 59
19	T	Peace Con. Brus. 1848	Dull	6 32
20	W	Sir C. Wren b. 1632	Win.	4 55
21	T	Bat of Trafalgar, 1805	Cold	6 36
22	F	A. Murray b. 1775	Rain	4 51
23	S	America disc. 1492	Win.	6 39
24	S	20 Sun. after Trinity	Fair	4 47
25	M	St. Crispin	Cha.	6 43
26	T	Riots at Bristol, 1831	Fair	4 43
27	W	Newsp. duty red. 1836	Fair	6 46
28	T	St. Simon & St. Jude	Fair	4 39
29	F	Dean Swift died, 1745	Rain	6 50
30	S	Towr. Armry. bt. 1841	Frost	4 36
31	S	21 Sun. after Trinity	Cha.	6 53

NOVEMBER 30 Days.
Last QR. 5d. 0·40 morn | 1st QR. 18d. 2·27 after
N. Moon 11d. 4·40 after | F. Moon 26d. 6·40 after

1	M	All Saints Day	Cha.	6 55
2	T	All Souls	Cold	4 30
3	W		Cha.	6 59
4	T	William III. lad. 1688	Cold	4 26
5	F	Gunpowder Plot, 1605	Rain	7 3
6	S	Leonard	Rain	4 23
7	S	22 Sun. after Trinity	Rain	7 6
8	M	Milton died, 1764	Clou.	4 20
9	T	Prince of Wales born	Clou.	7 9
10	W	O. Goldsmith b. 1728	Fog	4 16
11	T	St. Martin	Dull	7 13
12	F	R. Baxter b. 1615	Cold	4 13
13	S	Curran died, 1817	Rain	7 16
14	S	23 Sun. after Trinity	Fair	4 11
15	M	Machutus	Cha.	7 20
16	T		Fair	4 8
17	W		Frost	7 23
18	T	Sir D. Wilkie b. 1785	Frost	4 5
19	F	Thorwaldsen b. 1770	Frost	7 27
20	S	Edmund K. & Mart.	Cola	4 3
21	S	24 Sun. af. Trin.	Win.	7 30
22	M	[St. Cecilia	Show	4 1
23	T	[hole of Cal. 1756	Win.	7 33
24	W	416 Eng. in the black	Fair	3 59
25	T	Dr. I. Watts d. 1748	Frost	7 36
26	F	W. Cowper b. 1731	Show	3 57
27	S	Prs. M. Cam. b. 1833	Win.	7 40
28	S	1 Sunday in Advent	Frost	3 55
29	M	Polish Revolu. 1830	Show	7 42
30	T	St. Andrew	Cold	3 53

Battle of Navarino, 1827.

DECEMBER, 31 Days,
Last QR. 4d. 0·22 after | 1st QR. 1sd. 8·39 morn
N. Moon 11d. 3·31 morn | F. Moon 26d. 1·9 after

1	W	[Bonaparte c. 1804	Cold	7 46
2	T	Adelaide Q. D. d. 1849	Cold	3 52
3	F	Abdi. James II. 1688	Frost	7 48
4	S	Ld. Liverpool d. 1828	Rain	3 51
5	S	2 Sunday in Advent	Cold	7 51
6	M	Nicholas	Cold	3 50
7	T		Cold	7 53
8	W	Concept. of B. V. M.	Frost	3 50
9	T	Grouse Shooting ends	Snow	7 56
10	F	Milton born, 1608	Snow	3 49
11	S	Charles XII kill. 1718	Rain	7 58
12	S	3 Sunday in Advent	Fair	3 49
13	M	C. of Trent op. 1545	Fair	8 0
14	T		Fair	3 49
15	W	G. Romney b. 1734	Cold	8 1
16	T	John Selden b. 1584	Cha.	3 50
17	F	Sir H. Davy b. 1778	Snow	8 3
18	S	Bolivar died, 1830	Frost	3 50
19	S	4 Sunday in Advent	Sleet	8 5
20	M	Gray born, 1546	Cold	3 51
21	T	Thomas. Shor. day	Cold	8 6
22	W	Banks, Sculp. b. 1735	Fair	3 51
23	T	Sir R. Arkrght. b. 1782	Fair	8 7
24	F	Peace En. & U. S. 1804	Fair	3 52
25	S	Christmas Day	Frost	8 7
26	S	1 Sun. aft. Christmas	Fair	3 54
27	M	St. John [St. Stephen	Cold	8 8
28	T	Innocent	Frost	3 55
29	W	Wycliffe died, 1384	Frost	8 8
30	T	Robt. Boyle d. 1691	Cold	3 59
31	F	Silvester	Cold	8 8

PRUDENCE SAVES WHAT PASSION WASTES.

53

In 1851 wood-engraving was the dominating illustrative process. Whether they were
illustrations for the pictorial weeklies depicting events all over the world, as seen
through the artist's eye in London, or whether they were book illustrations of the
highest artistic standard, they were invariably cut in wood and printed from wood. The
wood-engraver worked at leisure on work of a high artistic standing, while several
engravers worked on a single image for newspapers in order to achieve speedier
production.

Fifty years after the Great Exhibition, two members of the famous Dalziel family — renowned for engraving in wood the work of some of the most prominent artists of the previous half-century — closed a chapter in the history of commercial wood-engraving.

'By the introduction of the various "processes" the days of wood engravings are practically over, and we have to bow down to the new light which we had long felt would come; and we need hardly say that, for the reproduction of good pen work, with the new process by line etching, the results are perfect.

'Also, when we look at the reproductions of tint drawings of artists of distinction, by the half-tone process, and when we think —beyond all this fine artistic work — of the vast mass of wonderful illustration given to the public, week by week, of every conceivable class of subject, direct from the camera, in which the draughtsman has no part at all, and this work is generally of singular beauty and truth — we feel that our occupation is gone. In saying this we wish to add that we hail with satisfaction the marvellous results from these many ingenious adaptations of photography; and the consequent wide spread of the art of illustration, which has ever been our greatest delight.'

Fifty years after this remarkable utterance, the camera has not only fundamentally changed all the reproduction methods, but one of the three major printing processes of our day, photogravure, would not have been possible without it.

In 1951, the camera is about to score its final triumph by taking its place in type setting, the invention of which over five centuries ago marked the origin of modern printing as we know it today.

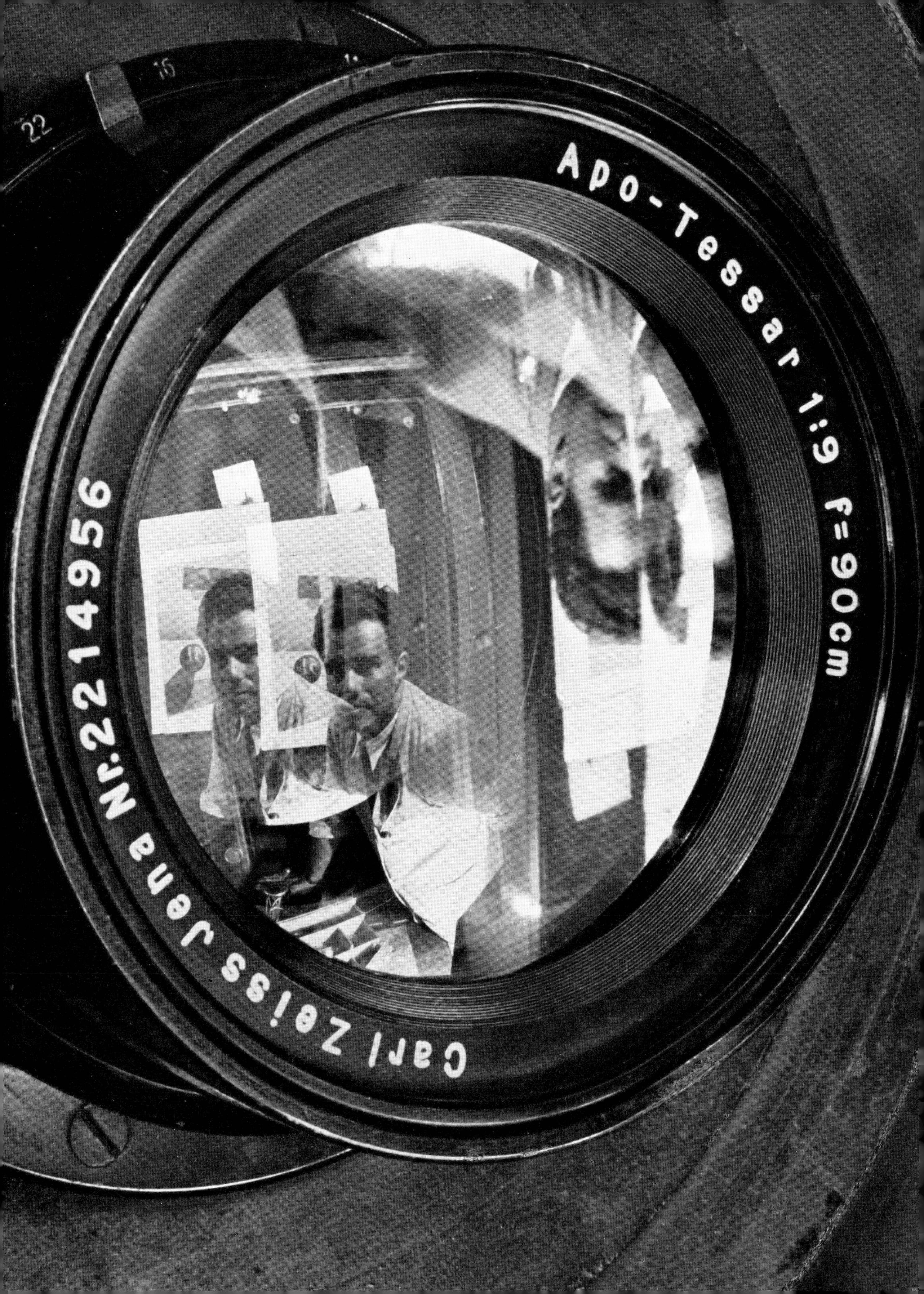
Apo-Tessar 1:9 f=90cm
Carl Zeiss Jena Nr. 2214956
22
16

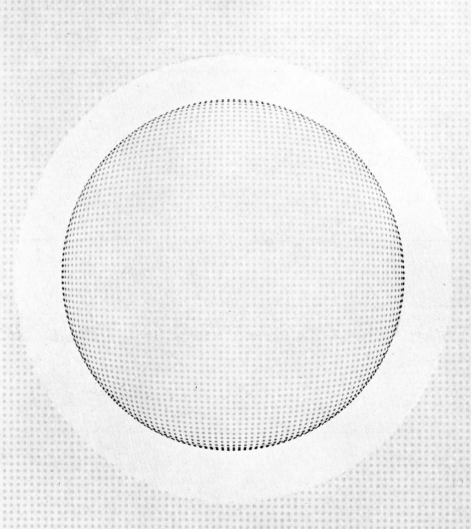

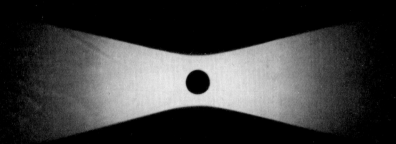

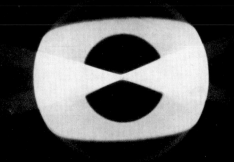

The constant use of line and the combination of hundreds of lines characterized all mid-nineteenth-century pictorial reproductions.

Tone values, light and shade, are the immense possibilities which have been given to us by the camera. Stiffness, indeed harshness, is the impression unwittingly caused by the wood-engraving illustration. Fancy was the foundation of pictorial reportage in the 1850's: the camera brought realism into the picture.

Events tens of thousands of miles away are placed before us, and mysteries of the universe are registered and conveyed to millions through the camera's eye and the printer's multiplication.

Decoration and ornament were the characteristic motifs embellishing — and confusing — the works of art of the mid-nineteenth century. The prevailing taste is clearly projected in the printer's conception of his work of that day. In the mid-twentieth century our aim is clarity of conception and presentation. The beauty of white paper can be emphasized and turned to the best advantage in the designer's hand, assisted by the accomplished work of present-day mechanical reproduction techniques.

nathan

59

Contrasting values can be expressed in one and the same colour with the combination of line and half-tone reproduction. The screen — an unknown mechanical element in the days of wood-engraving — is in its innumerable varieties at the service of the printer and designer.

Rhythm and balance can be conveyed with the greatest economy. Abstract elements and forms are but token symbols of factual motifs; and their right arrangement, giving equal justice to them all on the printed page, is the designer's function and justification of his rôle in the world of printing today.

Whilst some leading printers were using steam-driven printing presses in 1851, many still relied on hand-driven ones, the sheets being fed and gathered by the human hand. The average output was about 500 sheets per hour, the printing none too even. Today the electric motor provides steady high speed for the precision machine, which is the logical development of mechanical engineering. The sheets are automatically fed and delivered, the output being up to 5,000 sheets per hour.

Hand composing, the basic principles of which have not changed since the invention of movable type in the mid-fifteenth century, is comparatively slow. It calls for a considerable stock of type and material which wears out and has to be replaced at considerable cost. The mechanization of printing brought about a corresponding urge to speed up composing by mechanization.

Based on the earliest known typesetting machine constructed by Dr William Church of Massachusetts, the Young-Delcambre composing machine, with its piano-like keyboard, was patented in 1840. *It was the first effective typesetting machine* and was used in 1842 in London to set the *Family Herald*. The keyboard operator pressed the keys, and the types ran down inclined cylinders at the rear of the machine, where another operator gathered them at the end of the runway and then adjusted ('justified') them into lines of predetermined length. The types were placed in inclined channels and used time after time.

A COMPLETE SERIES OF UNIFORM FOUNTS.

𝔚. 𝔗𝔥𝔬𝔯𝔬𝔴𝔤𝔬𝔬𝔡 & 𝔠𝔬. 𝔥𝔞𝔟𝔢 𝔤𝔯𝔢𝔞𝔱 𝔭𝔩𝔢𝔞𝔰𝔲𝔯𝔢 𝔦𝔫 𝔰𝔲𝔟𝔪𝔦𝔱𝔱𝔦𝔫𝔤 𝔱𝔬 𝔱𝔥𝔢 𝔱𝔯𝔞𝔡𝔢 𝔞 𝔰𝔢𝔯𝔦𝔢𝔰 𝔬𝔣 𝔣𝔬𝔲𝔫𝔱𝔰 𝔬𝔣 𝔲𝔫𝔦𝔣𝔬𝔯𝔪 𝔰𝔥𝔞𝔭𝔢 𝔞𝔫𝔡 𝔠𝔥𝔞𝔯𝔞𝔠𝔱𝔢𝔯, 𝔰𝔬 𝔠𝔲𝔱, 𝔱𝔥𝔞𝔱 𝔴𝔥𝔦𝔩𝔢 𝔱𝔥𝔢𝔶 𝔭𝔯𝔢𝔰𝔢𝔫𝔱 𝔰𝔬𝔪𝔢 𝔠𝔩𝔞𝔦𝔪 𝔱𝔬 𝔢𝔩𝔢𝔤𝔞𝔫𝔠𝔢, 𝔠𝔞𝔫 𝔟𝔢 𝔠𝔬𝔫𝔣𝔦𝔡𝔢𝔫𝔱𝔩𝔶 𝔯𝔢=𝔠𝔬𝔪𝔪𝔢𝔫𝔡𝔢𝔡 𝔞𝔰 𝔭𝔬𝔰𝔰𝔢𝔰𝔰𝔦𝔫𝔤 𝔱𝔥𝔢 𝔤𝔯𝔢𝔞𝔱𝔢𝔰𝔱 𝔭𝔬𝔰𝔰𝔦𝔟𝔩𝔢 𝔡𝔲𝔯𝔞𝔟𝔦𝔩𝔦𝔱𝔶. 𝔓𝔯𝔬𝔭𝔯𝔦𝔢𝔱𝔬𝔯𝔰 𝔬𝔣 𝔑𝔢𝔴𝔰𝔭𝔞𝔭𝔢𝔯𝔰 𝔴𝔦𝔩𝔩 𝔣𝔦𝔫𝔡 𝔤𝔯𝔢𝔞𝔱 𝔞𝔡𝔳𝔞𝔫𝔱𝔞𝔤𝔢 𝔦𝔫 𝔞𝔡𝔬𝔭𝔱𝔦𝔫𝔤 𝔱𝔥𝔢𝔰𝔢 𝔣𝔬𝔲𝔫𝔱𝔰, 𝔞𝔰 𝔱𝔥𝔢𝔶 𝔞𝔳𝔬𝔦𝔡 𝔱𝔥𝔢 𝔲𝔫𝔰𝔦𝔤𝔥𝔱𝔩𝔶 𝔞𝔭𝔭𝔢𝔞𝔯𝔞𝔫𝔠𝔢 𝔴𝔥𝔢𝔯𝔢 𝔰𝔢𝔳𝔢𝔯𝔞𝔩 𝔣𝔬𝔲𝔫𝔱𝔰 𝔞𝔯𝔢 𝔲𝔰𝔢𝔡 𝔦𝔫 𝔱𝔥𝔢 𝔰𝔞𝔪𝔢 𝔭𝔞𝔤𝔢, 𝔢𝔞𝔠𝔥 𝔥𝔞𝔳𝔦𝔫𝔤 𝔞 𝔡𝔦𝔣𝔣𝔢𝔯𝔢𝔫𝔱 𝔰𝔥𝔞𝔭𝔢 𝔞𝔫𝔡 𝔤𝔢𝔫𝔢𝔯𝔞𝔩𝔩𝔶 𝔞 𝔱𝔬𝔱𝔞𝔩𝔩𝔶 𝔡𝔦𝔣𝔣𝔢𝔯𝔢𝔫𝔱 𝔠𝔥𝔞𝔯𝔞𝔠𝔱𝔢𝔯.

PICA, No. 1.

THE MESSENGERS OF JULIAN had been instructed to dispatch with diligence their important commission, but in their passage they were detained by the tedious and affected delays of the provincial governors, they were conducted by slow journeys from Constantinople, and when at length they were admitted to the presence of the emperor, they found that he had already conceived from the despatches of his own ministers, the most unfavourable opinion of his conduct, and of the army ; the letters were heard with impatience, the trembling messengers were dismissed with indignation and contempt, and the looks, the gestures, the furious language of the monarch, expressed the disorder of his soul, the domestic relation which might have reconciled the brother and the husband of the princess, was recently dissolved by her death; the EMPRESS EUSEBIA had preserved to the last moment of her life, the warm affection which she had conceived for him, and her mild influence might have moderated the resentment of a prince, who since her death was abandoned to his own passions, and to the arts of his eunuchs; but the terrors of a foreign invasion obliged him to suspend the punishment of a private enemy, he continued his march towards the confines of Persia, and thought it enough to signify the conditions which might entitle him and his guilty followers to the clemency of their offended sove-

SMALL PICA, No. 1.

THE MESSENGERS OF JULIAN had been instructed to execute, with diligence, their most important commission, but in their passage they were detained by the tedious and affected delays of the provincial governors, they were conducted by slow journeys from Constantinople, and, when at length they were admitted to the presence of the emperor, they found that he had already conceived from the despatches of his own ministers, the most unfavourable opinion of his conduct and of the army, the letters were heard with impatience, the trembling messengers were dismissed with indignation and contempt, and the looks, the gestures, the furious language of the monarch, expressed the disorder of his soul, for the domestic relation, which might have reconciled the brother and the husband of the princess was recently dissolved by her death ; the EMPRESS EUSEBIA had preserved to the last moment of her life the warm affection which she had conceived for him, and her mild influence might perhaps have moderated the resentment of a prince, who since her death was abandoned to his own passions, and the arts of his eunuchs ; but the terror of foreign invasion obliged him to suspend the punishment of a private enemy, he continued his march towards the confines of Persia, and thought it enough to signify the conditions which might entitle him and his guilty followers to the clemency of their much offended sovereign ; he required that the presumptuous rebel should instantly renounce the appella-

LONG PRIMER, No. 5.

THE MESSENGERS OF JULIAN had been instructed to execute with diligence their most important commission, but in their passage they were detained by the tedious or affected delays of the provincial governors they were conducted by slow journeys from Constantinople, and, when at length they were admitted into the presence of the emperor, they found that he had already conceived from the despatches of his ministers, the most unfavourable opinion of his conduct, and of the army ; the letters were heard with impatience, the trembling messengers were dismissed with indignation and contempt, and the looks, the gestures, the furious language of the monarch, expressed the disorder of his soul, the domestic relation which might have reconciled the brother and the husband of the princess, was recently dissolved by her death ; the EMPRESS EUSEBIA had preserved to the last moment of her life the warm affection which she had conceived for him, and her mild influence might have moderated the resentment of a prince who, since her death, was abandoned to his own passions, and to the arts of his eunuchs ; but the terrors of a foreign invasion obliged him to suspend the punishment of a private enemy he continued his march towards the confines of Persia, and thought it enough to signify the conditions which might entitle him, and his guilty followers, to the clemency of their offended sovereign ; he required that the presumptuous rebel should instantly renounce the appellation and rank of Augustus, which he had accepted as

⁎ *The Italic to each of these Founts is complete, and cut to correspond with the Roman.*

Lack of variety in the presentation of text matter, which relies mainly on 'modern' (vertical-stress) faces and great abundance of 'jobbing' (ornamental display) faces, characterizes mid-nineteenth century printing. In the mid-twentieth century the range of type faces used embraces designs revived from the greatest periods of typography as well as those of contemporaries, both for text *and* display purposes. This change was made possible by the introduction of mechanical composition.

THE MESSENGERS OF JULIAN had been instructed to dispatch with diligence their important commission, but in their passage they were detained by the tedious and affected delays of the provincial governors, they were conducted by slow journeys from Constantinople, and when at length they were admitted to the presence of the emperor, they found that he had already conceived from the despatches of his own ministers, the most unfavourable opinion of his conduct, and of the army; the letters were heard with impatience, the trembling messengers

THE MESSENGERS OF JULIAN had been instructed to dispatch with diligence their important commission, but in their passage they were detained by the tedious and affected delays of the provincial governors, they were conducted by slow journeys from Constantinople, and when at length they were admitted to the presence of the emperor, they found that he had already conceived from the despatches of his own ministers, the most unfavourable opinion of his conduct, and

THE MESSENGERS OF JULIAN had been instructed to dispatch with diligence their important commission, but in their passage they were detained by the tedious and affected delays of the provincial governors, they were conducted by slow journeys from Constantinople, and when at length they were admitted to the presence of the emperor, they found that he had already conceived from the despatches of his own ministers, the most unfavourable opinion of his conduct, and of the army; the letters were heard with impatience, the trembling messengers were dis-

THE MESSENGERS OF JULIAN had been instructed to dispatch with diligence their important commission, but in their passage they were detained by the tedious and affected delays of the provincial governors, they were conducted by slow journeys from Constantinople, and when at length they were admitted to the presence of the emperor, they found that he had already conceived from the despatches of his own ministers, the most unfavourable opinion of his conduct, and of

66

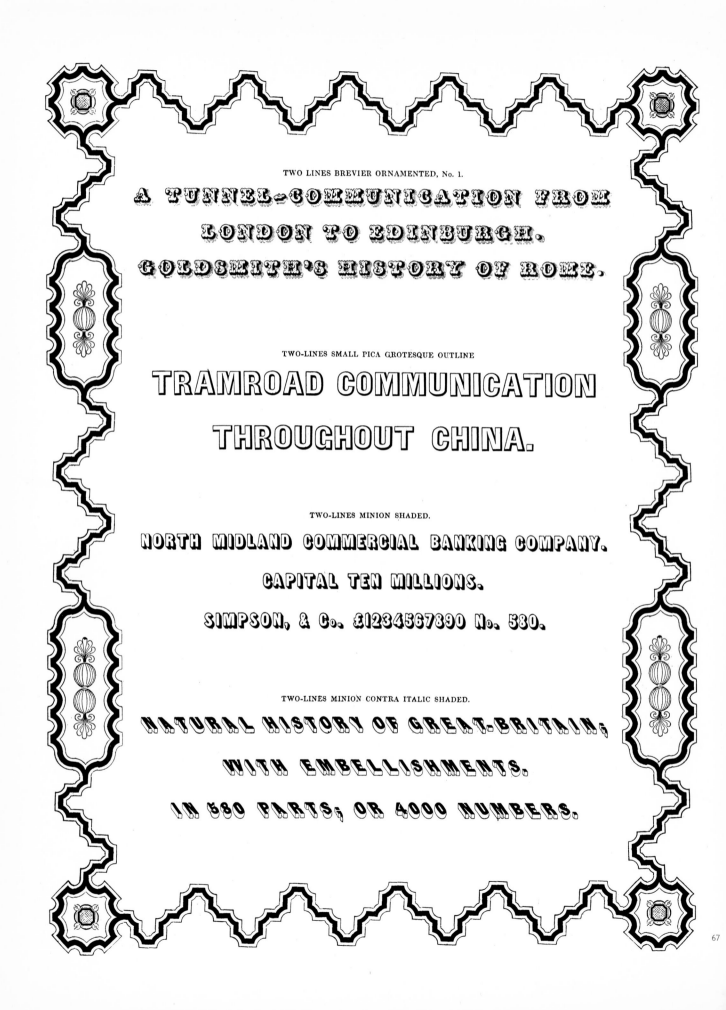

TWO LINES BREVIER ORNAMENTED, No. 1.

A TUNNEL-COMMUNICATION FROM

LONDON TO EDINBURGH.

GOLDSMITH'S HISTORY OF ROME.

TWO-LINES SMALL PICA GROTESQUE OUTLINE

TRAMROAD COMMUNICATION

THROUGHOUT CHINA.

TWO-LINES MINION SHADED.

NORTH MIDLAND COMMERCIAL BANKING COMPANY.

CAPITAL TEN MILLIONS.

SIMPSON, & Co. £1234567890 No. 580.

TWO-LINES MINION CONTRA ITALIC SHADED.

NATURAL HISTORY OF GREAT-BRITAIN,

WITH EMBELLISHMENTS,

IN 580 PARTS; OR 4000 NUMBERS.

'MONOTYPE'
PERPETUA

LIGHT TITLING SERIES NO. 480–18 TO 72 PT.

ABCDEFGHI
JKLMNOPQ
RSTUVWXY
Z&£.,.:;-!?—
1234567890

68

Left: Decorative display faces fashionable in 1851. — Right: Restrained titling version of text faces forms the basis of the printer's display in 1951.

A B E H
C D F
M K I
G L
J

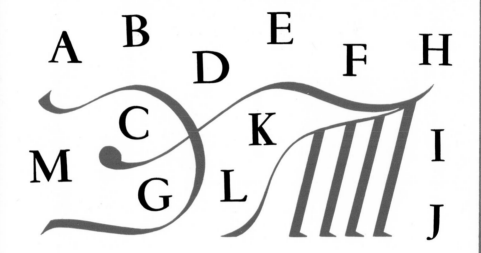

GARAMONT

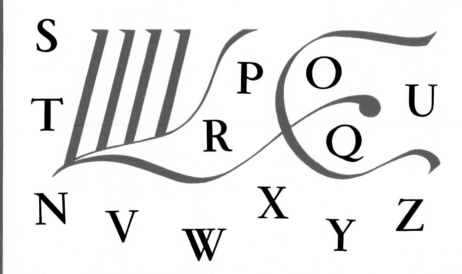

S O U
T P
R Q
N V X Y Z
W

TIMES

NEW

ROMAN

70

Left: Contemporary animated use of seventeenth-century French type face.
Right: Factual use of twentieth-century English type face.

The nineteenth century still belonged to the discoverer and to the explorer. One of the most characteristic phenomena of the mid-twentieth century, the mechanical age in which we live, is the combination of research and teamwork. Specialization has reached such a degree that to explain the mechanical complexities of present-day printing machinery and equipment would confuse rather than clarify the picture in the print-lover's and print-user's minds.

In designing the Royal Festival Hall, London, which aimed at acoustic perfection, the architect relied on the advice of experts to obtain correct resonance and equal clarity of sound in every seat. The result of co-ordination of knowledge in many spheres, the right choice of materials, their appropriate use and the ensuring that their appearance would be pleasing to the eye, it thus combines the functional with the aesthetic.

The printer of today relies to a large extent on continual research into problems of paper and ink performance, humidity control, a wide range of photo-mechanical processes, and the development of improved and synthetic materials for use in his plant. Thus, the achievement of a piece of printing which is as satisfying and pleasing to the eye as the music in the Royal Festival Hall is to the ear, calls for the printer's up-to-date knowledge of the stages or results of outside research and for a perfect co-ordination of brains and hands within his own workshop.

The satisfaction which can be given, however, does not wholly depend on mere technical accomplishment, for the forward-looking printer of today is equally interested in the aesthetic appearance of his work and is as much concerned with the matter as with the manner of what he prints.

In the main, he serves the fully mechanized machine in our day. Hand-composing is overshadowed by composing machines; the human hand cannot keep pace with the speed of presses fed by mechanical feeders. The demand for improved and new machinery outstrips supply, and the printer is hard put to it to co-ordinate his production on machinery which is partly new and partly old.

The near-monopoly of letterpress printing of the mid-nineteenth century is a matter of the past. Lithography has taken a place beside it, and the day seems near when its intrusion will be felt in the last stronghold of letterpress: book printing. With the increasing importance of the camera's work, both in pictorial magazines and pictorial catalogues, photogravure is coming to the fore at an accelerating speed.

The nineteenth century saw the mechanization of printing, type setting and reproduction techniques. The demand for metal in the printing trade has grown alarmingly in the last twenty-five years. The camera, which revolutionized and basically changed reproduction techniques, is now being applied to the composing of type faces. Several photo-composing machines are passing from the prototype stage into mass production. Their work may easily alter the whole aspect of printing in the second part of this century; and the impact of this change may be not only mechanical but aesthetic.

Letterpress composing machines were in the first place responsible for a revival of clear-cut classical type faces, which were followed by a wide range of newly designed type faces. In order to place themselves in a competitive position with type-setting machines, photo-composing machines appear to be presenting us with the same range of type faces as the printer is using today. The design of our present-day type faces was conceived for type that could be cut from metal and printed from metal in the letterpress process. Type set on the photo-composing machine is printed in offset or gravure which gives a softer impression to the type edges than letterpress. It is conceivable that, in order to meet this discrepancy of appearance, new type faces will be evolved for photo-composing machines and a new wave of hand lettering may be brought about.

Thus today the printer has printing presses at his disposal which turn out up to 5,000 sheets per hour. The presses are driven by electric power and they are mechanically fed and the sheets mechanically delivered. The preparation of the printing formes is assisted by ingenious mechanical devices. Whereas in 1851 the printer worked from foundry type faces which, in use again and again, became battered, today he is printing in the main from brand new founts produced afresh for each job by the type-setting machines. The surface of his printing forme is more even, the type faces are better spaced, and the surface from which he is printing is metal throughout. Whereas in 1851 the bulk of printed material was black and white, today he is able to give justice to multi-colour printing in all three major printing processes. Indeed, for a time, interest was focused on the attainment of perfection of colour printing to such an extent that black-and-white printing was temporarily neglected.

The lack of variety in body type faces and the overwhelming flow of display type faces of the 1850's have gone. Type appreciation, which started with the recutting of the main traditional type faces, led to the design and cutting of some of the finest new ones. By 1930 the printer was faced by an avalanche of new type faces, but the compositors were unconscious of the possibilities they afforded. The printer was better fitted to multiply than to create. He had the material, but he did not appreciate how to put it into use. The designer, the new man of a new era, stood by. In our day, the printer, with command over his equipment and faith in his technical ability, is increasingly aware of the creative aspect of his work.

The role of the designer in printing has become an ever-increasing one in the last twenty-five years and by now his place is established. The co-ordination of text and image, their formation into a single entity, is the designer's chief function in the printing trade. His success and usefulness largely depend upon his aesthetic and practical knowledge of the printer's materials. The attainment of the best aesthetic result with the most economic use of material and production time is the ideal to which both printer and print-buyer aspire. An intimate knowledge of reproduction techniques and printing methods will enable the designer to present his conception with a special view to the printing technique which can multiply it, not only most efficiently from the optical aspect, but most economically with regard to the quantity.

The various reproduction techniques of today are not only visually but economically competitive. The discrepancy in reproducing one and the same image by two different reproduction methods is sometimes greater in relation to cost than to appearance. Quantity is a determining factor owing to the fact that the initial cost varies considerably between the three major printing processes: letterpress, lithography and gravure. There is, however, a meeting point, which varies from job to job, where the reproduction cost of one and the same printed commodity is more or less equal in any of the three. But before arriving at this stage and passing it, the variation is very considerable indeed, giving advantage below it to the one technique and above it to another.

The problems involved, therefore, are both aesthetic and economic and they have to be faced from the start. The artist's creative mind is needed, working through his hands or through the camera's eye. Given an excellent camera and adequate studio equipment, there is hardly any limitation to the scope of this medium in the hands of a master. Colour photography is becoming one of the main competitors in many spheres of commercial design. It shows objects and subjects without evoking the element of suspicion created by the possible distortion or glorification of the designer's presentation. Once the photographer has laid aside his pride in successful glamorizing, and his tendency to 'show off' with the colours at his disposal, colour photography will undoubtedly present us with the most contemporary expression of both subjects and objects. The camera has no tradition: the artist has. If the artist's tradition can be put to the best use, coupled with the camera's mechanical magnitude, then photography will have the right to claim a place for itself as an art. Its work is of the greatest importance to the printer and provides him not only with his greatest possibilities but with his greatest reproduction problems. But as the solving of problems is the chief aim of the progressive printer, photography is bound to make one of the major contributions to the printer's progress.

The printer's standing today, both economically and socially, is very different from what it was in 1851. The value of his gross output in a typical year (1948) in the mid-twentieth century amounted to £128,633,000 in Great Britain alone. The cost of materials, fuel and electricity used ran into £34,804,000. He paid out £47,648,000 in wages and salaries to persons employed within his workshop; he gave employment in 2,322 establishments (not counting those which employed less than ten persons on the average during that year) to 159,218 people. The employer's share of contributions to all national insurance schemes payable during that year in respect of workers employed in the printing and allied trades in Great Britain amounted to £1,169,000.

In spite of shortages in both new and old machinery, the British printer spent £4,337,000 on machinery in that one year (£3,872,000 on new and £467,000 on second-hand). Frustrated and limited though he was by the scarcity of building materials and by the necessity for licences, he spent £816,000 on new buildings and extensions, excluding the site value.

These figures far from completely show the economic and social importance of the British printing trade in 1951, for they do not include printing, stereotyping and engraving plants engaged wholly or mainly in the printing or publishing of newspapers and periodicals, nor do they convey the enormous change, both in organization and working conditions, in printing plants, nor the improvements in the standard of living of those employed in the printing trade.

Publishers, who rely for their productions more than anyone else on the printing trade, are an equally important economic and social factor. The value of publishers' production in 1948 amounted to £20,901,000. Over the same period the publisher paid out £2,492,000 in wages and salaries to persons employed and a further £2,312,000 for authors' royalties, copyright dues, payments to contributors and editorial, artists' and readers' fees.

Thus through the production and distribution of printed material a considerable contribution is made year by year in sustaining literature and the arts.

In 1851 the printer stood on the threshold of the industrial revolution. His production was on the increase owing to mechanization, his services were increasingly in demand owing to growing commercial competition, and his products were absorbed by greater masses receiving higher wages.

In 1951 the printed word and the printed image are facing ever-increasing competition from the spoken word on the radio and the image on television. The fight against illiteracy is on: soon new masses and great continents will rely to a much larger extent on the printer's work. The loss on the one side may be counter-balanced by gain on the other. The printer's progress only partly depends on the progress of his equipment and of his material: it depends largely on his ability to open up the whole world for print.

The fundamental principle of good book-design is the co-ordination of all elements of the book. The factors to be determined are first, the right format; second, the choice of paper; and third, the choice of a suitable type face which will correspond with the style of the contents and print well on the paper which is chosen or available. Decision must be taken on the size of type and margins; whether to illustrate or not, and, if so, which illustration technique or techniques should be used and whether to print the illustrations with the text on the same paper, subject to the same reproduction technique being used for both, or, in the case of different techniques being used for text and illustration, whether to use corresponding or contrasting paper.

THE MEDITATIONS OF MARCUS AURELIUS. Fifty sonnets written in English in 1951, based on the Roman Emperor's original prose written in the second century A.D., clearly convey the printer's typographical problem, the type face to be used being indicated by the fact that the contents of the book are both *classical* and *contemporary*.

One of the sonnets is shown here in three type faces corresponding with this requirement. No. 73, Bembo, a type face which was designed and cut in England in the 1930's, based on a late fifteenth century type face cut in Italy for a text in Latin; No. 74, Diethelm Antiqua, the first post-war revival of the classical Roman type face; No. 75, Rotunda, a 1950 type face which attempts to give the feeling of a hand-written book. All three pages are printed in letterpress from type. The design on the title page has been engraved with the burin, not upon metal, but upon transparent plastic, and transferred to the plate to be printed with the accompanying text in offset lithography. All four pages, printed in two techniques, are on offset-cartridge.

THE MEDITATIONS OF MARCUS AURELIUS

FIFTY SONNETS

VI

Shouldst thou live for three thousand years in all,

Or more, no man loses a life but this,

Nor lives a new; long, short, are brought equal,

And towards all the present equal is.

The past is not the same; that lost only

A moment seems; nor past nor future man

Loses; for what a man has not, can he

Lose it? Can any take it: No one can.

Things from eternity the same are; they

Form circles; and no difference is shown

If man a hundred years or two survey

The same things, or for ever; and those mown

Soon, or long-lived, they lose the same. Man may

The present lose, the one thing his alone.

Shouldst thou live for three thousand years in all,

Or more, no man loses a life but this,

Nor lives a new; long, short, are brought equal,

And towards all the present equal is.

The past is not the same; that lost only

A moment seems; nor past nor future man

Loses; for what a man has not, can he

Lose it? Can any take it? No one can.

Things from eternity the same are; they

Form circles; and no difference is shown

If man a hundred years or two survey

The same things, or for ever; and those mown

Soon, or long-lived, they lose the same. Man may

The present lose, the one thing his alone.

THE MEDITATIONS

VI

Shouldst thou live for three thousand years in all,

Or more, no man loses a life but this,

Nor lives a new; long, short, are brought equal,

And towards all the present equal is.

The past is not the same; that lost only

A moment seems; nor past nor future man

Loses; for what a man has not, can he

Lose it? Can any take it? No one can.

Things from eternity the same are; they

Form circles; and no difference is shown

If man a hundred years or two survey

The same things, or for ever; and those mown

Soon, or long-lived, they lose the same. Man may

The present lose, the one thing his alone.

LE COQ ET LA PERLE

Un jour un coq détourna
Une perle, qu'il donna
Au beau premier lapidaire
Je la crois fine, dit-il;
Mais le moindre grain de mil
Seroit bien mieux mon affaire.

Un ignorant hérita
D'un manuscrit, qu'il porta
Chez son voisin le libraire.
Je crois, dit-il, qu'il est bon;
Mais le moindre ducaton
Seroit bien mieux mon affaire.

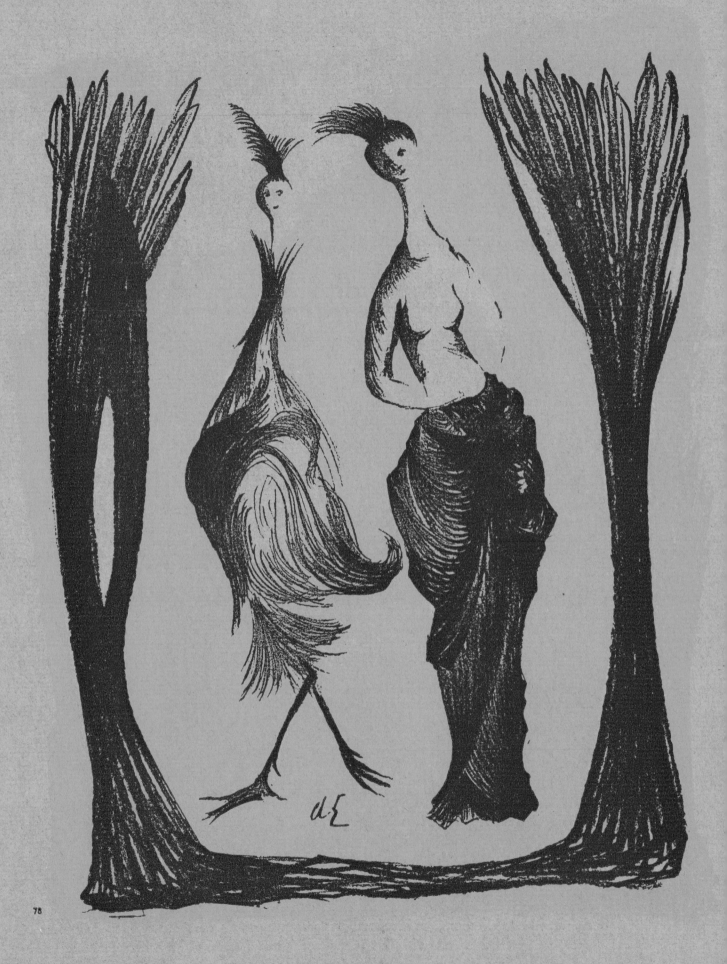

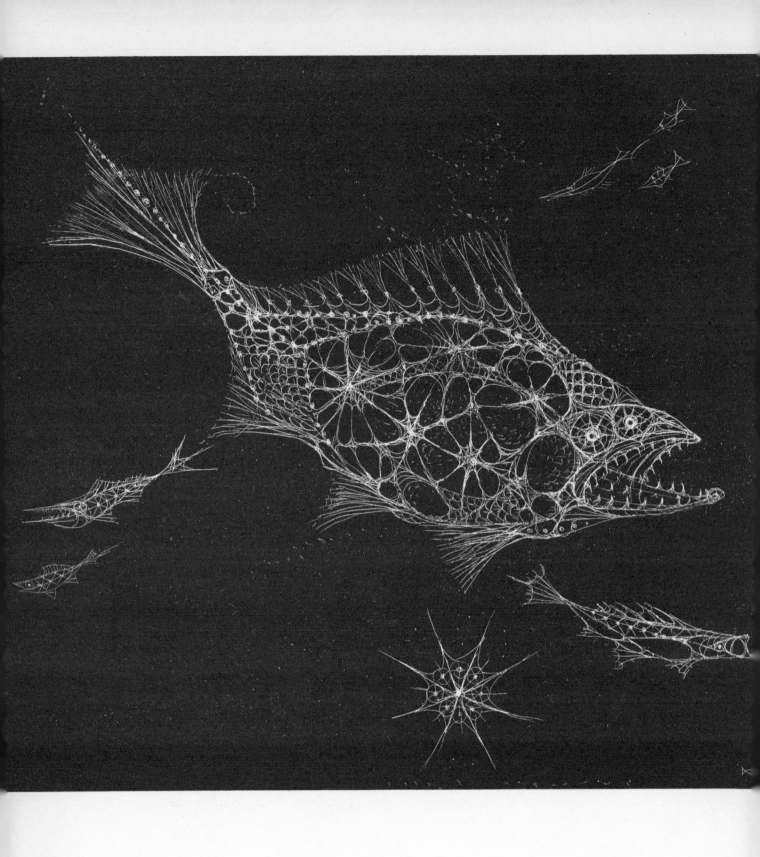

The reproduction of the artist's own work, without the inclusion or interference of mechanical media, largely depends on his knowledge and command of the reproductive crafts. Autolithography and wood-engraving are the ideal reproduction techniques to this end, the first for planographic printing, the second for letterpress.

The four original works reproduced here, the Cock, the Fish, the Cat and the Horses, are demonstrations of varied techniques — drawn or engraved by the artists on stone — of which lithography is capable. A contemporary revival of reproductive wood-engraving is shown later in the book.

Water-colour printing in letterpress, a method only too rarely used to achieve unusual and most attractive results on rough-surfaced paper, is demonstrated here by the reproductions of two drawings, 'The Lady and the Ostrich' and 'Peacocks', and by the printing of the text of the La Fontaine fable, Le Coq et La Perle. Preceding opening: Left: *Horses*, four-colour lithography drawn by the artist on to the stone. Right: Oil painting, *Portrait du facteur Roulin*, reproduced in four-colour photogravure.

P: PENGUINS IN SCOTLAND (EDINBURGH ZOO)

Just as the presentation of text depends on the right choice of type faces and their proper arrangement on the page, so does the presentation of an image, with or without the accompaniment of text.

Colour, as shown in this photograph (left), reproduced in four-colour photogravure, is one of the great attractions widely popularised through the improved ability both of the camera and of reproduction techniques.

But *black and white* photographs, when taken by artists, reproduced with skill and competence, printed on the right paper and displayed with care and imagination, are as attractive and striking as any. The following four photographs are reproduced in half-tone and printed in letterpress on white coated art paper.

T: SUNSET IN THE MOUNTAINS

87

Rivers, arise; whether thou be the son
Of utmost Tweed, or Oose, or gulfy Dun,
Or Trent, who, like some earth-born giant, spreads
His thirsty arms along the indented meads;
Or sullen Mole, that runneth underneath;
Or Severn swift, guilty of maiden's death;
Or rocky Avon, or of sedgy Lee,
Or coaly Tine, or ancient hallow'd Dee;
Or Humber loud, that keeps the Scythian's name;
Or Medway smooth, or royal-tower'd Thame.

                                                    Milton

CRYSTAL AND COMPANY

A FLOWER IN A CRYSTAL OUTLIVES SPRING

A FLOWER IN A CRYSTAL OUTLIVES SPRING

CRYSTAL AND COMPANY

Crystal

eft: Glass manufacturer's catalogue page: imaginative colour-photograph reproduced
four-colour gravure. Right: Glass manufacturer's catalogue cover or advertisement
r a periodical. The designer's conception reproduced in letterpress printing.

92

Contrast and Parallel. Left: Abstract expressed through the photographer's len
Right: Abstract presented by the painter's brush. Both reproduced in the bas
colours of yellow, red, blue and black of the four-colour process; the colour photogra
from the negative plates in half-tone; the painter's work by extensive and imaginati
use of a variety of mechanical tints.

Opera
LE COQ D'OR
Rimsky-Korsakov

94

Pen drawing with water-colour background reproduced from the same original in for
colour *letterpress* — yellow, red, blue and black. Printed on coated art paper.

Opera
LE COQ D'OR
Rimsky Korsakov

95

drawings with water-colour background reproduced from the same original in six-
our *offset* — yellow, red, pink, blue, light blue and black. Printed on coated art paper.

Contrast and Parallel. Left: Texture designed by the artist's hand. Right: Revealed through the camera's underwater shot. Both reproduced in six-colour *offset*. Printed on coated art paper.

99

Top: *The Lake of Lucerne* (*Switzerland*), a pastel drawing by the Swiss artist Alois Carigiet, is one of a series of eight landscapes, portraying the most characteristic parts of Switzerland, commissioned by the Swiss National Tourist Office. These drawings were to be reproduced in the size of 27 in. by 22 in., to serve the double purpose of (1) framed landscapes of Switzerland in travel offices and (2) the upper parts of posters, various announcements to be printed underneath the picture in black letterpress from type only. The choice of reproduction technique fell on photo-chrome, a partly manual lithographic printing process, *without screen*, which gives the picture great vividness and directness and is particularly suitable for reproducing paintings of a large size in short runs.

Left: *Paris*, a painting in gouache, prepared as a magazine cover. The reproduction is in photolithography, using screen, a more economical process than photochrome for large quantities in any size. (Six-colour printing on coated art paper). Following page: *Fortune* magazine cover, reproduction in photolithography, printed in the same colours as the *Paris* magazine cover, but on a non-coated offset cartridge paper.

MANUAL AND MECHANICAL REPRODUCTION PROCESSES

A design, drawn in reverse upon a block of wood, and the spaces between the lines cut away so that they remained in relief and formed a printing surface when inked and impressed upon paper — for four centuries this method constituted the simplest means of multiplying copies of a drawing. The design was cut upon the side grain of a soft wood with knives and gouges, and was largely reproductive work, in so far as the woodcutter aimed at making merely a facsimile of the drawing made upon the wood in pen or brush. Such designs were rendered mainly in outline and solid black, though simple tonal effects were indicated by closely packed lines.

It was Thomas Bewick who was credited with the introduction of the new method of wood-*engraving*, and thus founded the school of commercial engraving that flourished throughout the nineteenth century. He incised his designs upon the end grain of boxwood, employing a lozenge shaped graver of the type used for copper-engraving, in place of the knife. In the hands of Bewick and his followers the graver, combined with the hard boxwood, became an infinitely more expressive medium — a new graphic language rivalling the copper-engraving in variety of tonality and textural quality.

The school of creative engraving initiated by Bewick, however, was not to last. With the middle years of the Victorian era came the mechanization of the art, as the demand for speedily and cheaply produced blocks increased. The wood-engraver now concerned himself with purely facsimile reproduction, and his talent as a creative craftsman was subordinated to the conscientious imitation, in terms of engraving, of the artist's work, whatever the medium in which it had been drawn upon the wood.

Victorian commercial engraving, however, produced workmanship of a high order. Designs in books and periodicals, though often of small artistic merit, were invariably translated into the reproductive medium with consummate skill. Despite the progress that had been made in all branches of printing practice, the wood block still remained the only practicable means of reproducing illustrations on the letterpress machine. The steel-engraving, a favourite and typically Victorian method of reproduction, demanded

101

A contemporary revival of reproductive wood-engraving

separate printing by a less speedy operation, but was a far more flexible medium, capable of infinite graduations of tone of exquisite delicacy, and it would seem that the wood-engraver, as though impatient of his less responsive material, strained his medium to the utmost in striving to emulate his rival craftsman.

The invention of the process block in the latter years of the century provided a means of manufacturing illustration blocks with greater speed than had hitherto been possible, and quickly superseded wood-engraving as a commercial practice. By means of photography an image was transferred to a zinc plate and etched in relief in an acid bath. The new process was capable of producing a reasonably accurate facsimile of a line drawing, but it was not without its limitations. The action of the acid caused the black lines to lose their sharpness; the white lines thickened and lost character. The process block possessed little intrinsic beauty, and lacked the incisive and vibrant quality that was the chief characteristic of the engraving upon wood.

Scraper board drawing reproduced by process block. The
technique derives from the
woodcut, but is not purely
imitative. The brush lines of
the drawing have gained in
interest by being 'modelled'
by the scraping tool, and the
tones of grey are rendered
in a manner borrowed from
nineteenth-century wood-
engraving.

Cecil Keeling

A combination of process-engraving and hand-engraving. The block has been made from a drawing in pen line and solid black. The lines and areas of black on the zinco have been treated with the graver, and enlivened with a white line possessing a sharpness that would not have been achieved by etching alone. The artist has completed the work that the process-engraver had begun.

103

The illustrations show (*above*) the block made from the original drawing. (*Below*) the block after having been approved.

104

Example of a modern half-tone screen, in which the interpretation of tones is reminiscent of the technique of the nineteenth-century wood-engraver. Less monotonous in texture than the orthodox dot screen, such half-tones possess the advantage of the line block in yielding satisfactory impressions on inferior grades of paper, though successful reproduction is limited to drawings in a broad and well-contrasted treatment.

106

Right:
Wash and line drawing reproduced by aquatint half-tone screen.

Opposite page:
Two-colour lino-cut.

107

108

The Peep-show of our Times. A Look into the Unknown. Travel Prospectus.

The rousing of curiosity is the main objective of competitive travel publicity. An example of making the most of colours by the use of mechanical tint, and of presentation by novel folding and punching. Four-colour letterpress printing from line-blocks on coated art paper.

Printer's Progress

A selection of the original drawings and photographs

reproduced in **Printer's Progress** will be on view at

Park Works, Wisbech during the Festival of Britain

109

Twelve examples of contemporary design and letterpress printing, of which the first four are examples of typographical display in the traditional manner: 109 Invitation card, 110 Book advertisement, 111 Music cover, 112 Exhibition catalogue cover, 113 Announcement, 114 Opening of type face catalogue, 115 Technical advertisement, 116 Wine catalogue page, 117-118 Advertisements for periodicals, 119 Packaging catalogue cover (with original material).

Corinthian Editions announce NUMBER FIVE in the CORINTHIAN LIBRARY OF ILLUSTRATED CLASSICS:

MOLL FLANDERS

by DANIEL DEFOE, illustrated with lithographs by JOHN SUTTON

Titles already published are TRISTAM SHANDY by Laurence Sterne; VANITY FAIR by William Makepeace Thackeray; TREASURE ISLAND by Robert Louis Stevenson; TALES OF MYSTERY AND IMAGINATION by Edgar Allan Poe ✻ *Each volume Large Crown 8vo. Twenty-five shillings*

SIX

QUARTETS

FOR TWO VIOLINS

VIOLA AND VIOLONCELLO

COMPOSED AND DEDICATED TO

JOSEPH HAYDN

BY HIS FRIEND

WOLFGANG AMADEUS

MOZART

OPUS X

THE ARTS COUNCIL

Masterpieces
of
Victorian
Photography

VICTORIA AND ALBERT MUSEUM

MAY TO OCTOBER 1951

BEMBO

ALDUS MANUTIUS, the most illustrious printer of the late fifteenth century, employed Francesco Griffo to engrave the punches for the type to be used in *de Ætna*. 'Monotype' Bembo returns to this masterly source of great typography. *The chancery italic, with which it is mated, is of great distinction,* and together they grace the pages of many beautiful books.

One of many fine type faces available

form *and* colour

A B C D E F G H I J K L M N O P Q R S T U V W X Y Z

abcdefghijklmnopqrstuvwxyz

MAN-MADE MATERIAL

Rayon

Fine old Brown

SHERRY

N **B**

Nathan & Bates
LTD.

Manon

an early summer fragrance to enhance femininity

nash & blair

interior decoration

buckley street west one

Belrappa

NOTES AND ACKNOWLEDGEMENTS

(The numbers refer to illustrations)

No. I Enlargement of letterheading from the Great Exhibition.

No. II Pen and wash drawing reproduced in photo-lithography. Artist: Robert Turner.

1851

No. III Richard Doyle's drawings engraved in wood by the Dalziel Brothers.

No. 1 Detail (enlarged) from a wood-engraving published in the 19th July 1851 issue of 'The Illustrated Exhibitor'.

Nos. 2–5 Originals printed in black letterpress.

No. 6 Original printed in red, blue, and black letter-press.

No. 7 Original printed in green, black, and gold letterpress.

No. 8 Original printed in blue, heads embossed, and the whole surface varnished.

Nos. 8A, B, C Printed in black letterpress.

No. 8D Gold blocking on front and spine.

No. 9 Original printed in lithography.

Nos. 10–11 Originals printed in lithography.

Nos. 12–13 Text in letterpress printing carried out by H. Silverlock at the Great Exhibition; frontispiece engraving by J. R. Herbert after the original of H. Robinson; spine blocked in silver. *Reproduced from a copy in Mr John Carter's possession by his kind permission.*

No. 14 Letterpress printing — border: green, red and black; text: black only.

No. 15 The monthly of the printing trade. The leader deals with strikes; in the lower part of the second column, subscriptions in aid of the Metropolitan Typographical, Widow, Orphan or Nominee Fund are acknowledged to the following news-papers, which are still being published, in amalgamated form, today: 'Daily News', 'Morn-ing Post', 'Observer', 'Morning Chronicle.' *By courtesy of St Bride's Institute, London.*

No. 16 The front page picture — presumably engraved by several commercial wood-engravers — shows a carpet 'wrought by one hundred and fifty ladies and presented to Her Majesty the Queen' which was shown at the Great Exhibition. *By courtesy of the British Museum, London.*

No. 17 The illustrations are wood-engravings, with the exception of the two right bottom figures (wood-cuts) and the iron railing (No. 2 in column two) which is composed of typographical ornaments.

No. 18 The cover of 'Le Follet' printed in black (letter-press) on a yellow paper.

No. 19 First page of 'The Gentleman's Magazine of Fashion' printed in letterpress. The fashion plates (Nos. 18 and 19) are engravings which were specially pasted into the magazine between the letterpress pages. *By courtesy of the British Museum.*

Nos. 20–25 Cheap song-sheets, typical examples of popular printing, showing how the printer made do with material in hand originally used for very different purposes. Nos. 23 and 24 were most probably Hymn Book ornaments; and as the space was not filled in as required, other orna-mental motifs in the printer's hands were added (left and right top, No. 23; bottom centre, No. 24).

No. 26 Wood-engraving from Henry Mayhew's 'London Labour and the London Poor' — Long-Song Seller. The paper songs fluttered from a pole and the seller's cry was 'Three yards a penny!' Those engaged in the street sale of literature called themselves the 'paper-workers.'

No. 27 Both illustration and score were originally printed in lithography, black only.

Nos. 28–29 As far as can be ascertained, this is the first reproduction of an aerial view of London, taken by the daguerreotype process. No. 28, letterpress (the copy reproduced here seems to have been pasted on to a yellow paper with golden stars, a typical French decorative material of the '80's). No. 29, the map itself, is an engraving printed in deep sepia.

No. 30 A peep-show open, showing its construction.

No. 31 View through the hole into the peep-show. On the right, the Shah of Persia is seen leaving his carriage.

Nos. 32–33 Letterheadings available to visitors to the Great Exhibition: the first, wood-engraving; the second, lithography.

Nos. 34–39 Hand-outs at the Great Exhibition. Nos. 34 and 35 are wood-engravings with type, printed in letterpress: the first shows woman labour of the '50's, and the second child-labour. Nos. 36–37, lithography; the first, typical of lithographic treatment, the second, reminiscent of earlier steel-engraved work. No. 38, Catalogue pages. No. 39, top, lithography; bottom, wood-engrav-ing. The Victorian decorative appearance hides a perfectly functional construction.

Nos. 40–41 Catalogue pages. No. 40, wood-engraving. No. 41, top, steel-engraving; bottom, remarkable tabular typesetting.

No. 42 Classified advertisement page from 'The Times' of 21st August 1851. The arrangement is so accomplished that it could hardly be improved upon even in our day. *By courtesy of the Library of 'The Times'.*

No. 43 Typical example of mixture of type faces. Both advertisements original, black and white only, letterpress.

No. 44 Advertisement on the back page of book wrapper. The ornamental decorations are reminiscent of late eighteenth-century typography. Bottom left: wood-engraving illustration from Henry Mayhew's 'London Labour and the London Poor' — The Book Auctioneer. 'There's nothing in my trade that sells better, or indeed so well, as English classics', he stated. Some 1,375,920 volumes at an average price of 9d each were sold annually off seventy bookstalls and barrows in the streets of London in 1851, making a total of £51,597.

No. 45 Amongst the products advertised, Macassar Oil is still sold today in the package of 1851. The original advertisement was printed in black only on the back of the yellow paper-cover of 'Le Follet.' *By courtesy of the British Museum.*

Nos. 46–47 In order to achieve larger reproduction and better legibility of text, the top portion of this poster has been reproduced on the left-hand page and the bottom portion on the right-hand page. Printed in black only, letterpress.

No. 48 Top: railway notice, printed black only, letterpress. *By courtesy of W. Bemrose and Son,*

Derby. Bottom: front and back of the same railway ticket. *By courtesy of British Transport Commission, London.*

No. 49 Show card still in use in 1851. *Original in the collection of A. Rowland & Sons Ltd. and reproduced by their courtesy.*

No. 50 A Parlour Game showing famous towns or landscapes from the countries represented at the Great Exhibition. Lithography.

No. 51 The Almanack, the forerunner of the calendar of today.

No. 52 Illustration from 'David Copperfield', the most widely read book during the Great Exhibition (published late 1850). Wood-engraving. *By courtesy of Oxford University Press.*

Nos. 2, 3, 4, 5, 6, 7, 8, 8A–B–C–D, 9, 10, 11, 14, 17, 20, 21, 22, 23, 24, 25, 26, 27, 28, 29, 30–31, 32, 33, 43, 44, 46–47, 50, 51 *are reproduced by courtesy of the Victoria & Albert Museum, London.*

Nos. 34, 35, 36, 37, 38, 39, 40, 41 are reproduced from 'The Gilbart Prize Essay' by Granville Sharp. The circumstances under which this Essay was written, will be sufficiently explained by the following Extract from the 'Bankers' Magazine':

INDUSTRIAL EXHIBITION — BANKING PRIZE ESSAY — In our January number, we made the following announcement: 'We are authorized to announce that J. W. Gilbart, Esq., F.R.S., will present the sum of ONE HUNDRED POUNDS to the author of the best Essay which shall be written in reply to the following question: "In what way can any of the articles collected at the Industrial Exhibition of 1851 be rendered especially serviceable to the interests of *Practical Banking?*" '

For technical reasons, all illustrations of 1851 have been reproduced in this section of 'Printer's Progress 1851–1951' by photolithography and printed in offset. The references in the *Notes* are made to the reproduction techniques of the originals.

TRANSITION

No. 53 From Jackson's 'History of Wood-Engraving'. *By courtesy of St Bride's Institute.*

Nos. 54–57 Photographs by Werner Bischof.

Nos. 58–60 Abstracts by Jacques Nathan.

No. 61 Cylinder machine, *circa* 1835 (still in use in 1851). Wood-engraving.

No. 62 Control-panel of a rotation-machine, 1950 model. Photograph: Werner Bischof.

No. 63 Young-Delcambre composing machine. Wood-engraving. *By courtesy of Mr James Shand.*

No. 64 Monotype casting-machine. Photograph: Werner Bischof.

No. 65 Specimen page from W. Thorowgood & Co's type specimen book of 1847. *By courtesy of St Bride's Institute.*

No. 66 Specimen of some of the most widely used Monotype faces. (All four set in the same type-size, showing the variation in the number of letters per line).

No. 67 Specimen page from W. Thorowgood & Co's type specimen book of 1847. *By courtesy of St Bride's Institute.*

No. 68 A page of a Monotype specimen sheet.

No. 69 Decorative display panel, half-tone reproduction in two colours. *By courtesy of Deberny & Peignot, Paris.*

No. 70 Type specimen booklet printed in type. Designed for 'Printer's Progress 1851–1951' by Robert Turner.

The quotation facing illustration No. 54 is taken from 'The Brothers Dalziel: A Record of Work, 1840-1890' (Methuen & Co., London, 1891).

No. 71   Symbols of our age. Original water-colour composition by Robert Turner reproduced in two-colour photo-offset process.

No. 72   Original engraving by Cecil Keeling. Printed in offset, together with Bembo type.

No. 73   Bembo type of the Monotype Corporation, printed in letterpress. Sonnet from 'Marcus Aurelius, Meditations, 50 Sonnets', *by courtesy of Sylvan Press, London.*

No. 74   Diethelm Antiqua type face of the Haas Type Foundry, Munchenstein, Switzerland. Printed letterpress.

No. 75   Rotunda type face designed by Hans Vollenweider for the Johannespresse, Zurich. Printed letterpress.

No. 76   Le Coq et La Perle. Original in autolithography by Alois Carigiet. Printed in one colour by Wolfensberger, Zurich.

No. 77   'Le Coq et La Perle', La Fontaine's fable, illustrated by No. 76. Text set in Caslon Old Face Italic.

No. 78   The Lady and the Ostrich. Drawing by Dick Elffers. Water-colour printing in two colours. *Blocks by courtesy of Meijer, Wormerveer, Holland.*

Nos. 79–80 Originals by Hans Fischer. Printed in lithography from stone by Wolfensberger, Zurich.

No. 81   Drawing by Dick Elffers. Water-colour printing in one colour. *Block by courtesy of Meijer, Wormerveer.*

No. 82   Original autolithography by Hans Erni. Printed in four colours from stone by Wolfensberger, Zurich.

No. 83   Portrait du facteur Roulin painting by Van Gogh. *By courtesy of the Museum of Fine Arts, Boston, U.S.A.* Printed in four-colour photogravure by Conzett & Huber, Zurich.

No. 84   Colour-photography by Werner Bischof. Printed in four-colour photogravure by Conzett & Huber, Zurich.

Nos. 85–88 Photographs by Werner Bischof.

No. 89   From Milton's 'Anno Ætatis XIX'. Hand lettering by Robert Turner. Photogravure printing by Conzett & Huber, Zurich.

No. 90   Colour-photography by Werner Bischof. Printed in four-colour photogravure by Conzett & Huber, Zurich.

No. 91   Original by Jacques Nathan. Five-colour half-tone reproduction, printed letterpress.

No. 92   Colour-photograph by Werner Bischof. Letterpress printing.

No. 93   Design by Dick Elffers, showing some of the possibilities of mechanical tints. *By courtesy of G. H. Buhrmann's Papiergroothandel N.V., Amsterdam, Holland.*

Nos. 94–95 Gramophone record slipcase. Original by Robert Turner.

No. 96   Poster design by Savignac.

No. 97   Underwater colour-photograph by Werner Bischof. Varnished.

No. 98   Original by Villemot.

No. 99   Seven-colour photochrome reproduction by Orell-Fussli, Zurich, of a painting by Alois Carigiet. *Reproduced by courtesy of the Swiss National Tourist Office.*

No. 100   Original by Jacques Nathan.

Nos. 101–106 Originals by Cecil Keeling.

No. 102   *By courtesy of The Shell Petroleum Company Ltd, London*

No. 107   Design by Dick Elffers. *By courtesy of the Amsterdam Type Foundry, Holland.*

No. 108   Original by Robert Turner.

Nos. 109–112 Original designs by Cecil Keeling:
No. 109 set in Gill Sans Serif type.
No. 110 set in Caslon Old Face.
No. 111 set in Bodoni and Bodoni Book.
No. 112 set in Modern Condensed and Bodoni Book.

No. 113   Original design by Robert Turner. Set in Bembo type.

No. 114   Drawing and typography by Dick Elffers. *By courtesy of the Amsterdam Type Foundry.*

No. 115   Design by Otto Treumann. *By courtesy of N.V. International Rayon-Verkoopkantoor, Arnhem, Holland.*

Nos. 116–118 Originals by Robert Turner.

No. 119   Photograph by Werner Bischof. *By courtesy of Belrappa, London.*

No. 120   Pattern design by Kato Lukats, printed on metal foil. *By courtesy of Belrappa, London.*

The type face used throughout for the text is the Bodoni Book of the Monotype Corporation.

The endpapers were printed direct from mull in letterpress.

PRINTER'S PROGRESS 1851-1951

was produced in the printing works of

BALDING & MANSELL

ENGLAND

———————————

It must be acknowledged that the scope of this volume

would have been limited if the reproduction processes demonstrated

therein were confined solely to those in use in any given printing house.

Almost every available process has therefore been included,

and full details of the co-operation so readily given by other printers

on the inserts appear in Notes and Acknowledgements.

———————————

WERNER BISCHOF, CECIL KEELING and ROBERT TURNER

contributed original work and assisted with the general presentation;

ALOIS CARIGIET, HANS ERNI, HANS FISCHER and JACQUES NATHAN

prepared originals; DICK ELFFERS, SAVIGNAC, VILLEMOT and OTTO TREUMANN

readily consented to the reproduction and adaptation of their work,

and valuable critical advice on the historical aspects of the text

was given by ELLIC HOWE